Six-Way paragraphs

100 Passages for Developing the Six Essential Categories of Comprehension

Walter Pauk, Ph.D.
Professor of Education
Director, Reading-Study Center
Cornell University

Jamestown Publishers
Providence, Rhode Island

SIX-WAY PARAGRAPHS

100 PASSAGES FOR DEVELOPING
THE SIX ESSENTIAL CATEGORIES
OF COMPREHENSION

Cover Design by Stephen R. Anthony
Text Design and Illustrations by Mary M. Macdonald

Printed in the United States

Preface

Learning by doing is still the most reliable method for mastering new skills or for putting fine edges on old ones. But mastery is dependent on more than just doing. It is dependent on structured materials and guided instruction. This book meets all these requirements: textbook-type passages for doing, and uniquely-designed six-way questions for structure, and for guidance.

Although I assume complete responsibility for the faults of this book, I am happy to acknowledge my indebtedness to students and colleagues, for many of its strong points. The students in all my classes have been helpful in their suggestions and enthusiasm. Graduate students, colleagues, and teachers, too numerous to mention individually, provided criticism when I needed it most. I wish to single out Walter Brownsword, former chairman of the English Department of Rhode Island Junior College, for especial thanks for refining the six-way questions. The staff of Jamestown Publishers has been helpful in its editorial duties. To all I am grateful.

Finally, grateful acknowledgment is made to *Aramco World Magazine* and to *Petroleum Today* for permission to use and adapt the materials in this book.

Walter Pauk

Ithaca, New York
February 1974

Contents

Introduction

The paragraph! That's the working-unit of both writer and reader. The writer works hard to put meaning into the paragraph; the reader works hard to take meaning out of it. Though they work at opposite tasks, the work of each is closely related. Actually, to understand better the job of the reader, one must first understand better the job of the writer. So, let us look briefly at the writer's job.

To make his meaning clear, a writer knows that he must follow certain basic principles. First, he knows that he must develop only one main idea per paragraph. This principle is so important that he knows it backwards, too. He knows that he must not try to develop two main ideas in the same, single paragraph.

The next important principle he knows is that the topic of each main idea must be stated in a topic sentence and that such a sentence best serves its function by coming at or near the beginning of its paragraph. He knows, too, that the more clearly he can state the topic of his paragraph in an opening sentence, the more effective he will be in developing a meaningful, well-organized paragraph.

One word of warning to the reader: there is no guarantee that the topic sentence will always be the first sentence of a paragraph. Occasionally, a writer will start off with an introductory or a transitional sentence. Then, it is up to the reader to spot such a sentence, and recognize it for what it is.

The topic sentence may be placed in several other positions in a paragraph. It may be placed in the middle, or even at the very end. If it appears at the end, though it may still be a topic sentence in form, in terms of function, it is more rightfully a *restatement*. Whenever the end position is chosen, it is chosen to give the restatement especial emphasis.

Finally, a paragraph may not have a topic sentence in it at all. Some writers purposely leave out such sentences, presumably, to lend an air of sophistication to their writing. But, in such cases, inferring a topic sentence may not be so difficult as it may at first appear. Here's why. Inside information has it that many such professional writers actually do write topic sentences, but on separate scraps of paper. They then place one of the scraps at the head of a sheet and use the topic sentence to guide their thoughts in the construction of the paragraph. With the paragraph written and the topic sentence having served its purpose, the scrap is discarded. The end result is a paragraph without a visible topic sentence, but the paragraph, nonetheless, has embedded in it all the clues that an alert reader needs for making an accurate inference.

Actually, there is nothing especially important in recognizing or inferring a topic sentence for its own sake. The important thing for the reader is in his *using* the topic sentence as a quick means for establishing a focal point around which to cluster the meaning of the subsequent words and sentences that he reads. Here's the double-edged sword again: just as the writer used the topic sentence to provide focus and structure for presenting his meaning, so the perceptive reader can use the topic sentence for focus and structure to gain meaning.

Up to this point, the reader, having looked secretly over the writer's shoulder, should have learned two exceedingly valuable secrets: first, that he should always look for only *one* main idea in each paragraph; and secondly, that he should use the topic sentence to lead him to the topic of each paragraph.

Now, there is more to a writer's job than just writing paragraphs consisting of only bare topic sentences and main ideas. The balance of his job deals with *developing* each main idea through the use of supporting material which amplifies and clarifies the main idea and many times makes it more vivid and memorable.

To support his main ideas, a writer may use a variety of forms. One of the most common forms to support a main idea is the *example*. Examples help to illustrate the main idea more vividly. Other supporting materials are anecdotes, incidents, jokes, allusions, comparisons, contrasts, analogies, definitions, exceptions, logic, and so forth.

To summarize, the reader should have learned from the writer that a textbook-type paragraph usually contains these three elements: a topic sentence, a main idea, and supporting material. Knowing this, the reader should use the topic sentence to lead him to the main idea. Once he grasps the main idea, then everything else is supporting material used to illustrate, amplify, and qualify the main idea. So, in the final analysis, the reader must be able to separate the main idea from the supporting material, yet see the relationship between them.

Organization of the Text

The Three Criteria

One hundred of the very best passages were selected from an original stock of over three hundred. Each of these expository passages had to meet the following criteria: *mature interest level, appropriate readability level,* and *factual accuracy of contents.*

The mature interest level was insured by choosing passages from journals or magazines that were written expressly for mature, intelligent adults in the first place.

The readability level of each passage was determined by the use of the Dale-Chall readability formula, thus enabling the arrangement of passages in an ascending order of difficulty. Those passages that exceeded prescribed difficulty levels, were eliminated.

The factual accuracy of these passages is high because they were written by professional writers and scholars who have researched each article. The bonus effect of these non-fictional passages is that students will be building up not only their reading skills, but also their backgrounds.

The Questions

At the end of each passage, there are six questions to answer. The six questions will always be within the framework of the following six categories: subject matter; main ideas; supporting details; conclusions; clarifying devices; and vocabulary in context. By repeated practice with questions within these six essential categories, students will develop an active, searching attitude when reading other expository prose. These questions will help them become aware of what they are reading at the time of the actual perception of the words and phrases, thus setting the stage for high comprehension.

The Diagnostic Chart

Fast and sure improvement in reading comprehension can be made by using the Diagnostic Chart to identify relative strengths and weaknesses. The Diagnostic Chart is a very efficient instrument. Here is why and how it works.

The questions for every passage are always in the same order. For example, the question designed to teach the skill of recognizing the *main idea* is always in the number two position, and the skill of drawing *conclusions* is always in the number four position, and so on. This innovation of ordering the questions sets the stage for the functioning of the Diagnostic Chart.

The Diagnostic Chart functions automatically when the letters of answers are placed in the proper spaces. Even after completing one passage, the chart will reveal the types of questions answered correctly, as well as, the types answered incorrectly. But more important for the long run, is that the chart will identify the types of questions that are missed consistently. Such identification is possible after three or more passages have been completed. By then, a pattern should be observable. For example, if a student's answers to question number four (drawing conclusions) were incorrect for all three passages, the weakness would be obvious immediately. Once a weakness in drawing conclusions, for example, is ascertained, the following procedure is recommended: First, he should reread the question; then, with the correct answer in mind, he should reread the entire passage trying to perceive how the author actually did lead to or imply the correct conclusion. Second, on succeeding passages, he should put forth extra effort to answer correctly the questions pertaining to drawing conclusions. Third, if the difficulty continues, he should arrange a conference with his instructor.

To the Student

How to Get the Most
For Your Time and Effort

Some people call these techniques "tricks of the trade." In academic circles, however, they are called "scholarly principles." It doesn't matter what they are called. What really matters is that they work.

Title Scrutiny

Just the other day at lunch, one old-timer, an English professor already retired some fifteen years, did use the word "trick." He said, "I didn't discover the trick until I was an assistant professor. Wished I had known about it as a freshman." He explained the trick by saying, "The first thing I do is to read the title of everything. Then, I spend a few seconds thinking about it." He continued, "Remember! An author spends more time thinking up a just-right title than he does thinking about any other single portion of the paper. He tries to pack into the title as much meaning as he can. So, I take advantage of it, by thinking about the title, even for a few seconds. I try to take out of it as much meaning as I can, thus getting a head-start on the whole process of reading."

"Title scrutiny does one more thing for you that most people don't know about. It starts you off concentrating on the story or article before you actually begin reading it. Why? A few moments thinking about the title fills your head so full of thoughts about the story that there's no room for anything else to get in to break concentration. That's a trick, too," he chuckled. "People talk about having trouble concentrating when reading. That's one trouble I never had," he said.

The Dot System

Here is a system that will speed up your reading and sharpen your comprehension skills. After spending a few seconds with the title, move rapidly through the passage. Then, without looking back over the passage, answer all of the questions by placing a dot in the square beside the option that you think is correct. The dot will indicate your unofficial answer.

This system is a game you play. You will find that you will try extra hard to grasp and retain more and more as you progress through the book. This extra effort will, in fact, make you a better reader permanently.

The Check-Mark System

Having answered all of the questions tentatively with a dot, now reread the passage and, this time, indicate your official answer by placing a check mark (✓) in the square next to the option that you think is correct. This check-marked answer will count toward your final score.

The Diagnostic Chart

Transfer your official answers to the Diagnostic Chart. Do this by writing your official answer in the upper portion of each block. When scoring your answers, do NOT use an X-mark for incorrect, nor a C-mark for correct. Instead, use the following method. If the answer is correct, make no additional mark within the answer block. So, if correct, the bottom portion will be unmarked. But, if your official answer is incorrect, then write the correct answer-letter in the bottom portion of the specific block. Your incorrect answers are the ones to worry about. So, your incorrect answers will have in the one block, your

own answer and the answer gotten from the answer key. This sets the stage for the next step: "Taking Corrective Action."

Taking Corrective Action

Your incorrect answers can provide you with a rich opportunity for self-learning. To take this opportunity, then, investigate all incorrect answers by going back to the original question to read the correct option several times. With the correct option well in mind, turn back to the passage itself to see why the approved answer is correct and analyze why you chose the incorrect option.

Graphing and Recording Your Progress

It would be good to have both the Diagnostic Chart and Comprehension Graph directly exposed in front of you for instant use and reference. So, tear out the page bearing both. (The Answer Key and Diagnostic Chart pages have been perforated to permit removal.) This will make it easier to record your official answers onto it, to check the answers with the Answer Key, to refer to it as your eyes check back and forth during the corrective action, and to translate your comprehension percentage into a line—a graphic representation—on your Comprehension Graph.

Six-Way Paragraphs

The Steps in a Nutshell

Here's how to get the most for your time and effort:

1. **Title Scrutiny:** Get from the title the meaning that the author put into it.

2. **The Dot System:** After your first fast reading, answer all of the questions with the unofficial dot.

3. **The Check-Mark System:** Reread the passage and, this time, put a check mark (✓) in a block to indicate your official answer.

4. **The Diagnostic Chart:** Record your official answer in the proper blocks of the Diagnostic Chart.

5. **The Answer Key:** Use your answer key in the way suggested on page 12.

6. **Corrective Action:** Investigate all incorrect answers. Reread the passage. Analyze your mistakes.

7. **Graphing Your Progress:** Record your comprehension score on the graph.

1. LOUIS BRAILLE, ALPHABET MAKER

It took a blind man to lead the way in devising a system that permits the blind to read. Louis Braille, a normal, healthy, French child at birth, became sightless when he was only three. At ten, he was placed in a home for the blind, a ward of society. But young Louis had great talent. He became a skilled musician. Soon he was appointed a church organist in Paris.

When he was twenty-five, he became a teacher of the blind. To help his students with their studies, he laboriously developed a crude alphabet of raised indentations on stiff paper so that his young <u>flock</u> could study both written and musical works. This, perfected, became the Braille system.

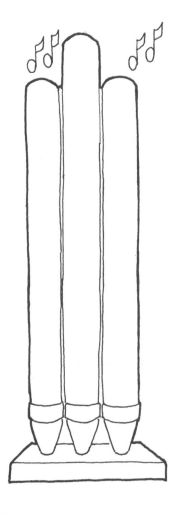

1. The passage is mainly about
   - ☐ a. the Braille alphabet.
   - ☐ b. blind people.
   - ☐ c. Louis Braille.
   - ☐ d. the method permitting the blind to "see."

2. What is the main idea of the passage?
   - ☐ a. Blind people can be quite talented and even become church organists.
   - ☐ b. Louis Braille was a blind man.
   - ☐ c. It was a blind person that developed a reading method for blind people.
   - ☐ d. Blind people can read.

3. You wouldn't expect that
   - ☐ a. Louis learned to read before he was blind.
   - ☐ b. Mr. Braille wanted to help the blind to read.
   - ☐ c. Braille was one of the most difficult alphabets to read.
   - ☐ d. every blind person can read Braille.

4. It is probable that
   - ☐ a. all blind people do read Braille.
   - ☐ b. sign language is more useful than Braille to the blind.
   - ☐ c. most students realized that Mr. Braille developed the Braille alphabet.
   - ☐ d. Louis Braille wouldn't have developed the alphabet if he had had perfect sight.

5. The author makes his point by
   - ☐ a. comparison and contrast.
   - ☐ b. negative arguments.
   - ☐ c. autobiographical observation.
   - ☐ d. a personal case study.

6. The best meaning of <u>flock</u> in this passage is
   - ☐ a. a group of sheep.
   - ☐ b. a number of blind students.
   - ☐ c. a number of wards of the society.
   - ☐ d. several blind musicians.

CATEGORIES OF COMPREHENSION QUESTIONS

No. 1: Subject Matter	No. 3: Supporting Details	No. 5: Clarifying Devices
No. 2: Main Idea	No. 4: Conclusion	No. 6: Vocabulary in Context

2. ANCIENT FIRE FIGHTING

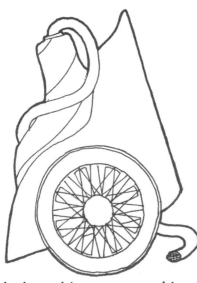

It may seem surprising, but the fact is that the fire engine goes back to the time of Christ. Caesar Augustus (63 B.C.–14 A.D.) formed the first fire department in Rome. Seven hundred firemen lived in firehouses throughout the city. They used a wheeled machine which squirted water on fires. This "water squirt" was a huge syringe. The bulb may have been as long as a man's body, and it was squeezed by means of a giant screw turned by a fireman. Such squirts—and even hand syringes three feet long—were in use when the Great Fire swept London in 1666. The hand squirts were held by two firemen while a third worked the plunger—much as you push the plunger in a garden spray gun today. It took the London fire—and great fires in other growing cities—to awaken people to the need for better equipment.

1. This passage is mainly about
   ☐ a. fire engines.
   ☐ b. the Great Fire.
   ☐ c. types of fires.
   ☐ d. firemen.

2. According to the author
   ☐ a. water pumps are ancient fire fighting tools.
   ☐ b. the Great Fire must have killed a lot of people.
   ☐ c. the water squirt was an unsuccessful fire hose.
   ☐ d. fires will never be prevented no matter what measures are taken.

3. Which of the following is not true?
   ☐ a. The water squirt was used only in Rome.
   ☐ b. Fire engines go back to the time of Christ.
   ☐ c. Caesar formed the first fire department in Rome.
   ☐ d. A water squirt is a huge syringe.

4. From this passage the reader could conclude that in 63 B.C.−14 A.D.,
   ☐ a. a controlled method of fire fighting was necessary.
   ☐ b. people wanted to prevent forest fires.
   ☐ c. Augustus was a very smart man.
   ☐ d. many lives were saved from fire.

5. In the paragraph the author uses which of the following?
   ☐ a. Comparison
   ☐ b. Surprising facts
   ☐ c. Personal opinion
   ☐ d. Common sense

6. One type of syringe described is a
   ☐ a. water pail.
   ☐ b. unique type of vacuum.
   ☐ c. special type of hose.
   ☐ d. tube with a piston that can draw or eject liquids.

CATEGORIES OF COMPREHENSION QUESTIONS

No. 1: Subject Matter	No. 3: Supporting Details	No. 5: Clarifying Devices
No. 2: Main Idea	No. 4: Conclusion	No. 6: Vocabulary in Context

3. WHAT ABOUT FROST?

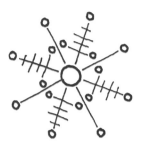

Wind—even the slightest of breezes—can prevent frost. That's because wind is like a spoon in your cup of tea: it stirs things around and brings down a lot of the warm air that often floats just above housetops and trees.

It may seem odd but ice itself sometimes can protect crops from frost! Some growers actually spray their crops with water on a freezing night. Water freezes quickly on the plants—and then a strange thing happens. As long as ice stays wet, it can't get colder than 32 degrees, a temperature many plants can stand. If the ice ever became entirely frozen and dry, it might drop many degrees lower, ruining the plants. But by continually spraying water on the ice, the growers keep it from going below 32 degrees even if the air is much colder. This may frustrate Jack Frost, but it saves the plants.

This strange kind of "ice blanket" works only on plants that are strong enough to stand the weight of frozen spray. The system is used even to protect banana plants on some Central American plantations.

1. The best title would be:
   - ☐ a. Jack Frost Triumphs Again.
   - ☐ b. Ice Can Be Nice.
   - ☐ c. Battle of the Farmer.
   - ☐ d. The Helpless Plant.

2. This passage is intended
   - ☐ a. to explain why some plants can withstand ice.
   - ☐ b. to show how ice forms.
   - ☐ c. to give tips on preserving crops.
   - ☐ d. to show that frost can be prevented.

3. Ice can save plants rather than destroy them if the plants are
   - ☐ a. strong enough to support it.
   - ☐ b. sprayed periodically.
   - ☐ c. accumstomed to frost.
   - ☐ d. quickly defrosted.

4. It can be concluded from the passage that ice would not protect from frost
   - ☐ a. banana trees.
   - ☐ b. fir trees.
   - ☐ c. delicate rose bushes.
   - ☐ d. apple orchards.

5. The author writes his passage with the use of
   - ☐ a. cause and effect relationships.
   - ☐ b. personal opinions.
   - ☐ c. arguments and proof.
   - ☐ d. comparison and contrast.

6. As used in this passage, ice blanket means
   - ☐ a. a cold blanket.
   - ☐ b. a spray of frost.
   - ☐ c. a covering of ice.
   - ☐ d. a thermal blanket.

CATEGORIES OF COMPREHENSION QUESTIONS

| No. 1: Subject Matter | No. 3: Supporting Details | No. 5: Clarifying Devices |
| No. 2: Main Idea | No. 4: Conclusion | No. 6: Vocabulary in Context |

4. THE MILLER'S PROBLEM

Early European windmills became a problem when winds reached gale force. Unless the canvas sails of the windmill were furled, the entire structure could be torn from its foundation and tossed on its side. Sea captains faced the same danger. Unless they trimmed their sails, the masts would squirm out of their sockets and tumble overboard. The captain could pipe his riggers aloft to shorten canvas, but the miller's task was not that simple. First, he had to shut down his mill. This was achieved by braking the wind shaft. The brakes were two wooden blocks called cheeks. If the cheeks were applied too quickly, the sails would come to an abrupt stop, and the wind would tear them to shreds. If the sails withstood the blast, the grindstone, stopping just as abruptly, could leap from its mounting and crash through the side of the mill, often taking life and limb.

Both dangers were removed by redesigning the sails. In place of canvas, wooden blinds were adopted. As modern window blinds control the passage of light, so the wooden mill blinds controlled the passage of air. If a storm arose, the blinds were opened and the blast passed harmlessly through the sails. If the winds were calm, the blinds were closed to capture every breath.

1. The best title for this selection would be:
   - ☐ a. Designing Windmill Sails.
   - ☐ b. Stopping Windmill Arms.
   - ☐ c. The Problem of High Winds and Its Solution.
   - ☐ d. Furling the Ship's Canvas.

2. The principal advantage of the wooden blinds in place of cloth sails was that
   - ☐ a. the wood lasted longer than the cloth.
   - ☐ b. the wood was heavier than the cloth.
   - ☐ c. when wooden blinds were used, the cheeks were not necessary.
   - ☐ d. the wooden blinds could adapt to wind conditions.

3. The brakes used to slow down the windmill shaft were called
   - ☐ a. shoes.
   - ☐ b. axles.
   - ☐ c. cheeks.
   - ☐ d. discs.

4. A windmill is similar to a sailing ship because
   - ☐ a. both are wind powered.
   - ☐ b. the sails of both are identical.
   - ☐ c. both use wooden brakes.
   - ☐ d. both use blinds to control wind flow.

5. The function of the second paragraph is
   - ☐ a. to illustrate a point made in the first.
   - ☐ b. to explain a solution to a problem raised in the first.
   - ☐ c. to show what happens when the wind blows too hard.
   - ☐ d. to illustrate why the windmill was never a very satisfactory device.

6. When a captain pipes his riggers aloft, he
   - ☐ a. signals his crew.
   - ☐ b. supplies his men with pipes.
   - ☐ c. plays music.
   - ☐ d. raises the mast automatically.

CATEGORIES OF COMPREHENSION QUESTIONS

No. 1: Subject Matter	No. 3: Supporting Details	No. 5: Clarifying Devices
No. 2: Main Idea	No. 4: Conclusion	No. 6: Vocabulary in Context

5. A BEAN TAKES A BOW

In the wild state, cocoa trees grow from 25 to 40 feet tall. Under cultivation, they are kept pruned to a height of about 15 feet. They require a mean temperature of about 80 degrees and cannot stand direct sunlight, particularly when young. Usually they grow best in the shade of tall mango, banana, rubber, or breadfruit trees.

The trees bloom and grow pods throughout the year, although their yield is highest during two peak periods. Their five-petal blossoms are waxy pink and the color of the leaves ranges from pale rose to red and green. The silvery bark of the tree trunk adds even more color, as do clinging moss and rainbow lichens.

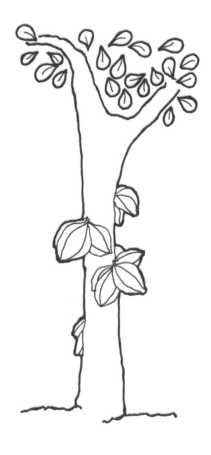

1. This passage deals mainly with the
   - ☐ a. cultivation of the cocoa bean.
   - ☐ b. pruning of the cocoa tree.
   - ☐ c. cocoa tree.
   - ☐ d. cocoa beans and tree.

2. The main idea of this passage is that
   - ☐ a. there are some distinct characteristics of the cocoa tree.
   - ☐ b. cocoa trees produce cocoa beans.
   - ☐ c. cocoa trees cannot stand direct sunlight.
   - ☐ d. it takes a great deal of work to produce coffee and cocoa.

3. When the author refers to the mean temperature, he is referring to the
   - ☐ a. temperature of the shade under the banana, mango, etc. trees.
   - ☐ b. temperature that the trees are made to grow in.
   - ☐ c. exact temperature necessary for cocoa trees to survive.
   - ☐ d. average temperature suitable for the growth of cocoa trees.

4. It is possible to conclude that the cocoa tree
   - ☐ a. must always be in a climate of 80 degrees.
   - ☐ b. has an improved yield when pruned.
   - ☐ c. grows under another tree to get the nutrients in the soil.
   - ☐ d. has been cultivated by men living only in the cocoa jungles.

5. The author develops his paragraph by using
   - ☐ a. comparison.
   - ☐ b. contrast.
   - ☐ c. arguments.
   - ☐ d. description.

6. To be kept pruned means
   - ☐ a. to be kept dried out.
   - ☐ b. to have the trunk scraped.
   - ☐ c. to be fertilized with prunes.
   - ☐ d. to have branches cut off.

CATEGORIES OF COMPREHENSION QUESTIONS		
No. 1: Subject Matter	No. 3: Supporting Details	No. 5: Clarifying Devices
No. 2: Main Idea	No. 4: Conclusion	No. 6: Vocabulary in Context

6. STAGECOACH HERO

As shipments of gold dust by stagecoach increased, so did attempts to waylay the coaches by gangs of highwaymen. Charley Parkhurst, a stage driver in California, who was widely known for his driving skill, was once stopped by highwaymen. Charley gave up the express box on demand and added, "I wasn't expecting this, but the next time you stop me I'll be ready for you." Charley was, too. Parkhurst shot the leader of the ill-starred gang that stopped his stage the next time and whipped his team right through the others, scattering them. What made Charley's feat all the more remarkable was revealed at his death in 1879. The doctor's death certificate showed that Charley, old rough-and-tumble Charley, was actually Charlotte Parkhurst.

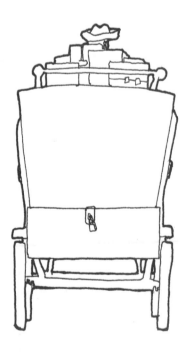

1. The best title for this paragraph would be:
   - ☐ a. The Dangers of Stage Travel.
   - ☐ b. The Triumph of Charley Parkhurst.
   - ☐ c. The Death of Charley Parkhurst.
   - ☐ d. The Last Great Stage Robbery.

2. This paragraph illustrates that
   - ☐ a. women would have made better stagecoach drivers.
   - ☐ b. stage passengers were in great danger.
   - ☐ c. gold shipments were often targets for theft.
   - ☐ d. men "rode shotgun" to protect the driver.

3. The gangs of highwaymen wanted the
   - ☐ a. express box.
   - ☐ b. gold dust.
   - ☐ c. passengers' cash.
   - ☐ d. coach itself.

4. The main requirement for a stage coach driver was to be
   - ☐ a. a man.
   - ☐ b. a skilled driver.
   - ☐ c. remarkable.
   - ☐ d. a good shot.

5. The adjective "ill-starred" describes the gang's
   - ☐ a. intentions.
   - ☐ b. reputation.
   - ☐ c. luck.
   - ☐ d. skill.

6. As used in this passage, to waylay seems to mean
   - ☐ a. to attack and capture.
   - ☐ b. to chase and destroy.
   - ☐ c. to attack from hiding and rob.
   - ☐ d. to force to turn around and go back.

CATEGORIES OF COMPREHENSION QUESTIONS

No. 1: Subject Matter	No. 3: Supporting Details	No. 5: Clarifying Devices
No. 2: Main Idea	No. 4: Conclusion	No. 6: Vocabulary in Context

7. THE LONG AND SHORT OF IT

The "rule of thumb" is no idle idiom. The early inch was the width of a man's thumb. In the fourteenth century, England's Edward II decreed it should be "three barley corns, round and dry, placed end-to-end lengthwise." He didn't say from which part of the ear the kernels should come, or how much they should be worn down at the end to make them "round," but the directions seemed sufficient for the needs of the day. A king, of course, could make such decrees and expect them to be reasonably followed. But where there was no central authority strong enough to set up standards and enforce their use and uniformity, a standardized system of weights and measures had little chance against the <u>inconsistent</u> arm and foot lengths of tribal chiefs.

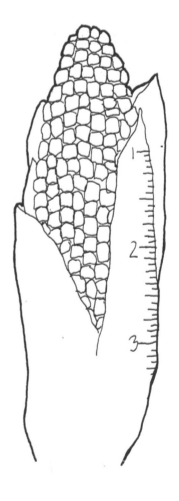

1. This article is mainly concerned with
   ☐ a. the decrees of Edward II.
   ☐ b. round barley corns.
   ☐ c. problems of measurement.
   ☐ d. thumb widths.

2. Edward II recognized the need for
   ☐ a. a standard inch.
   ☐ b. his power to be absolute.
   ☐ c. all of his decrees to be followed.
   ☐ d. a process for rounding barley corns.

3. The author states that
   ☐ a. thumbs were about an inch long.
   ☐ b. barley corns were always the same size.
   ☐ c. barley corns were all round.
   ☐ d. not all chiefs were the same size.

4. Necessary to the development of standardized measures is
   ☐ a. a strong central authority.
   ☐ b. the rule set up by Edward II.
   ☐ c. the use of barley corns.
   ☐ d. uniform arm length.

5. To develop his point, the author uses
   ☐ a. comparison and contrast.
   ☐ b. arguments and proof.
   ☐ c. historical facts.
   ☐ d. common-sense knowledge.

6. The word inconsistent is closest in meaning to
   ☐ a. systematic.
   ☐ b. different.
   ☐ c. unreasonable.
   ☐ d. ridiculous.

CATEGORIES OF COMPREHENSION QUESTIONS

No. 1: Subject Matter	No. 3: Supporting Details	No. 5: Clarifying Devices
No. 2: Main Idea	No. 4: Conclusion	No. 6: Vocabulary in Context

8. TASTY WEEDS

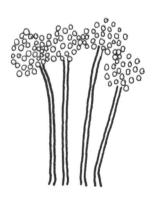

It's a rare person nowadays who can find the ingredients for an appetizing meal in an untilled field or a vacant lot. But that doesn't mean they aren't there. One of the most maligned of weeds, the dandelion, is a living supermarket. The leaves are delicious in salads, the golden blossoms make an interesting wine, and both the roots and leaves are used in medicines. (And children find it fun to blow the puffs of seed onto their neighbor's lawn!) Chicory, wild lettuce, and sheep sorrel also go well with French dressing, while curled dock, lamb's quarter, pigweed, and sow thistle add flavor and substance to a soup or stew. Many weed-eaters prefer lamb's quarter to spinach as a cooked vegetable. The evening primrose is a weed in the United States, but in England and Holland, where it is grown commercially, it is considered a delicacy.

1. This passage is mainly about
   □ a. untilled fields.
   □ b. using dandelions in salads.
   □ c. edible weeds.
   □ d. weeds used in cooking.

2. The dandelion is
   □ a. used most often in salads.
   □ b. considered a delicacy outside of the United States.
   □ c. one of many useful weeds.
   □ d. a favorite weed in supermarkets.

3. The dandelion is called a living supermarket because
   □ a. it grows in combination with other weeds.
   □ b. it is grown commercially.
   □ c. of its high nutritional value.
   □ d. of its many possible uses.

4. From the passage, the reader can conclude that the weeds mentioned are
   □ a. better tasting than most vegetables.
   □ b. not fatal if consumed.
   □ c. easier to pick than to buy from the store.
   □ d. more nutritious than most vegetables.

5. To make his main point, the author uses
   □ a. limited but good examples.
   □ b. complex reasoning.
   □ c. mostly his own opinions.
   □ d. detailed comparisons.

6. The word <u>maligned</u>, as used in the passage, means
   □ a. falsely undervalued.
   □ b. tasty.
   □ c. inexpensively grown.
   □ d. systematically destroyed.

CATEGORIES OF COMPREHENSION QUESTIONS		
No. 1: Subject Matter	No. 3: Supporting Details	No. 5: Clarifying Devices
No. 2: Main Idea	No. 4: Conclusion	No. 6: Vocabulary in Context

9. KNIVES, FORKS AND SPOONS

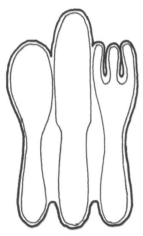

Knives and spoons were already in general use when forks were introduced to the general public in England only 250 years ago.

For a long time the use of forks was scorned. Men continued to eat with their fingers, calling forks effeminate. The English clergy even branded them as sacrilegious because they were a substitute for human fingers.

Nevertheless forks slowly gained acceptance. In those days forks usually had only two tines; these were long and dangerous-looking. If you would see what a Dutch table fork of 1650 looked like, open your cupboard and take out your carving fork. This is a throwback to early table forks, which, in turn, were throwbacks to a vicious twin-pointed battle spear. The four-tined forks that we know today did not come into general use until well over a century ago. As a matter of fact, the four-tined fork is about as new as the steam engine.

1. This article could best be titled:
   - ☐ a. Tine and Tine Again.
   - ☐ b. Fingers Are Better.
   - ☐ c. The Fork Revolution.
   - ☐ d. Man's Greatest Invention.

2. The fork
   - ☐ a. was used in Anglican ceremonies.
   - ☐ b. took Europe by storm.
   - ☐ c. was invented by the Dutch.
   - ☐ d. gained acceptance very slowly.

3. Dutch table forks
   - ☐ a. were sometimes used as battle spears.
   - ☐ b. were used only for carving.
   - ☐ c. originally had only two tines.
   - ☐ d. were more efficient than modern forks.

4. Forks
   - ☐ a. are the "newest" eating utensils.
   - ☐ b. used to be four-tined.
   - ☐ c. are enjoying renewed popularity.
   - ☐ d. are closely related to spoons.

5. The author uses
   - ☐ a. unkind sarcasm.
   - ☐ b. straightforward examples.
   - ☐ c. critical remarks.
   - ☐ d. deep insights.

6. The word throwback, as used in the passage, means
   - ☐ a. an object which is able to return to the sender.
   - ☐ b. something which bounces.
   - ☐ c. an object originating in an earlier similar object.
   - ☐ d. a valuable antique.

CATEGORIES OF COMPREHENSION QUESTIONS

No. 1: Subject Matter	No. 3: Supporting Details	No. 5: Clarifying Devices
No. 2: Main Idea	No. 4: Conclusion	No. 6: Vocabulary in Context

10. APPLE CIDER

When apples are made into cider, they are first washed, and then fed into a grinder and reduced to a pulp which is called "cheese." In horse-and-buggy days most farms used mail-order hand-grinders. Nowadays, these are hard to come by, but for small batches a hand meat-grinder will do. In any case, the youngest and most energetic members of the crew can usually be induced to take over this phase of the operation.

The next and crucial step is to place the "cheese" in the press. When a simple hand screw-press is used, the apple pulp may be held in a slatted basket. In a cider mill's hydraulic press the "cheese" is placed in cloths on slatted frames which are stacked one upon the other. In either type the juice passes between the slats and is collected at the base of the press as cider.

The pressed pulp, called pomace, must be disposed of at once, for this pomace will attract every buzzing yellowjacket within miles.

1. This selection is mostly about apple cider and its
   - ☐ a. history.
   - ☐ b. usefulness.
   - ☐ c. production.
   - ☐ d. variety.

2. Basically, apple cider is made by
   - ☐ a. squeezing the "cheese" through a press and collecting the juice.
   - ☐ b. cutting the apples into pieces and soaking them in water.
   - ☐ c. boiling the juice out of the "cheese."
   - ☐ d. grating the "cheese" and letting the juice drip out naturally.

3. The pressed pulp is
   - ☐ a. made into cider.
   - ☐ b. used in baking.
   - ☐ c. thrown out.
   - ☐ d. squeezed a second time.

4. Cider pressing is
   - ☐ a. a fun sport.
   - ☐ b. a backbreaking task.
   - ☐ c. an involved process, using both people and machines.
   - ☐ d. an interesting and unusual way of preserving apples.

5. The author explains cider pressing through
   - ☐ a. a series of images.
   - ☐ b. a description of the process.
   - ☐ c. an explanation of its history.
   - ☐ d. a set of examples.

6. The pomace of an apple is the
   - ☐ a. leftover cores.
   - ☐ b. sweet smell.
   - ☐ c. pressed pulp.
   - ☐ d. mass of stems and skins.

CATEGORIES OF COMPREHENSION QUESTIONS

No. 1: Subject Matter	No. 3: Supporting Details	No. 5: Clarifying Devices
No. 2: Main Idea	No. 4: Conclusion	No. 6: Vocabulary in Context

11. RUDOLPH'S RUGGED RELATIVES

Lapland is not a recognized country. It is a large area north of the Arctic Circle made up of sections of Norway, Sweden, Finland and Russia. It has no government of its own. In this flat, marshy, almost treeless land where the sun doesn't set for three months of the year, where it never rises for another three, the Lapp herdsman and his reindeer live much as they have lived for hundreds, even thousands of years. It is the Lapp who, over the centuries, has tamed the reindeer. For as the reindeer went northward, following the moss, so the prehistoric Lapp hunters followed the herds. The Lapps originally came from east of the Urals, in Russia, and a few thousand years later were followed by the Finns, over the same route. Being more advanced culturally, and an agricultural people, the Finns gradually forced the Lapps farther and farther into the icy wastes of northern Norway, Sweden, Finland and Russia; the Lapps, in their own language, call themselves "the banished." The four groups of Lapps are closely connected racially, wear similar costumes, and live, as they have for centuries, almost wholly on the reindeer. Each of the three Scandinavian countries has respected their unique, almost Stone Age culture, and, though governing them, has left them to develop very much along their own lines.

1. The best title for this selection could be:
   - ☐ a. Persecution of the Lapps.
   - ☐ b. The Reindeer of Lapland.
   - ☐ c. Migration of the Lapps.
   - ☐ d. The Culture of Lapland.

2. The single most important factor in distinguishing the Lapps from their neighbors is their
   - ☐ a. advanced form of agriculture.
   - ☐ b. almost primitive lifestyle.
   - ☐ c. skill in hunting reindeer.
   - ☐ d. primitive language.

3. The Finns and Lapps share a common
   - ☐ a. language.
   - ☐ b. style of dress.
   - ☐ c. culture.
   - ☐ d. origin.

4. The government of Lapland can best be described as
   - ☐ a. independent of Scandinavian influence.
   - ☐ b. dominated by Communist influence.
   - ☐ c. fairly democratic.
   - ☐ d. virtually nonexistent.

5. The author mentions the migration of the Finns in order to explain the Lapps'
   - ☐ a. living in the far north.
   - ☐ b. dependence on reindeer.
   - ☐ c. Stone Age culture.
   - ☐ d. racial connection to them.

6. The word banished, as used in this passage, is closest in meaning to
   - ☐ a. hopeless.
   - ☐ b. forsaken.
   - ☐ c. expelled.
   - ☐ d. persecuted.

CATEGORIES OF COMPREHENSION QUESTIONS

No. 1: Subject Matter	No. 3: Supporting Details	No. 5: Clarifying Devices
No. 2: Main Idea	No. 4: Conclusion	No. 6: Vocabulary in Context

12. A NEW WAY TO PLOW?

Over 100 years ago on a day late in 1859 the great test came. In those days of ox-drawn plows farmers were accustomed to spending an entire day plowing a single acre. An acre, in fact, had originally been defined as the amount of land a farmer could plow in a day.

On the day of the test a thousand farmers left their oxen at home and gathered in a field near Lancaster, England, to hoot or cheer while Fawkes' great "field locomotive" was fired up. Fawkes sat at the controls, gave two toots of the whistle and opened the throttle. The <u>contraption</u>, which looked like a monster iron smokestack on wheels, began to move. Ridicule turned to awe. Rapidly it gained speed and soon the coal-fired steam locomotive was racing across the field faster than men could walk. And the farmers saw that it was pulling not one "bottom" as plowmen call their plows, but *eight*.

Farmers couldn't believe their eyes. Fawkes plowed an acre in twelve minutes flat. Even today that's an amazing performance. A farmer pulling three bottoms behind a modern tractor allows about two and a half hours for plowing an acre.

Fawkes' wonder was too big, too costly, and too hard to repair. Its great weight packed the fields too tight, and it fell into mudholes. Thus it failed.

1. The best title for this selection would be:
   - ☐ a. The Field Locomotive.
   - ☐ b. The Power-Driven Cultivator.
   - ☐ c. Ox-Drawn Plows.
   - ☐ d. The Failure of Steam Plows.

2. The invention of the steam-driven locomotive capable of pulling a number of bottoms or plows was significant because
   - ☐ a. it did more work in less time.
   - ☐ b. it did not require men to operate it.
   - ☐ c. it was not operated by hand.
   - ☐ d. its design was perfect.

3. Which of the following factors was not responsible for the failure of the steam-driven field locomotive?
   - ☐ a. Its weight
   - ☐ b. Its size
   - ☐ c. Its speed
   - ☐ d. Its price

4. The fact that tractor-drawn triple plows are used today suggests that compared to steam-driven field locomotives, modern tractors
   - ☐ a. are more efficient.
   - ☐ b. are not so powerful.
   - ☐ c. do more in less time.
   - ☐ d. are easier to run.

5. The author mentions the modern farmer's output to show
   - ☐ a. how advanced the modern farmer is.
   - ☐ b. the difficulty of a farmer's work.
   - ☐ c. the relative power of the field locomotive and today's tractor.
   - ☐ d. how efficient the farmer has become.

6. As used in this selection, contraption seems to mean
   - ☐ a. well-designed machinery.
   - ☐ b. imposing mechanical device.
   - ☐ c. unusual and odd-looking machine.
   - ☐ d. useless pile of junk.

CATEGORIES OF COMPREHENSION QUESTIONS

No. 1: Subject Matter	No. 3: Supporting Details	No. 5: Clarifying Devices
No. 2: Main Idea	No. 4: Conclusion	No. 6: Vocabulary in Context

13. A LINE ON KITES

Actually, there are four basic types of kites: flat, bowed or angled, nonrigid, and novelty kites.

The flat kite, the simplest of all, is the only kite that requires a tail. Without a tail made of knotted strips of cloth, ribbon, or stringed paper, a flat kite would loop and dive erratically—if it stayed in the air at all.

Americans are more familiar with bowed and angled kites. The basic bowed kite is a four-sided, diamond-shaped kite made of paper or cloth stretched on a cross-frame of softwood sticks. The shorter stick is bent and tied into a bow. The box kite is one of the most common of the angled kites. It consists of a rectangular, box-shaped frame of wood with a wide band of cloth or paper at each end. The midsection of the box is open. Bowed kites are used much more than box kites in this country. Few of the many other types of bowed or angled kites are ever flown—not even the tetrahedral kite, which was invented by a famous American, Alexander Graham Bell.

The nonrigid kite has only recently joined the ranks of high-flyers in this country. Any kite without a rigid framework qualifies, although parachute-shaped models seem to have the edge.

Novelty kites are most popular in the Orient. By adding extra branches to the wooden frame, attaching decorations, and cutting designs in the surface, kites are made to look like birds, fish, dragons, and even people.

1. The passage is essentially a
   - ☐ a. description of the four basic types of kites.
   - ☐ b. guide to kite-flying.
   - ☐ c. history of kite development.
   - ☐ d. scientific analysis of the mechanism of flight.

2. In this passage the author tries to
   - ☐ a. explore the many kinds of problems involved in kite-flying.
   - ☐ b. explain the different constructions of the four types of kites.
   - ☐ c. give an explanation for the popularity of kite-flying.
   - ☐ d. invent a colorful new way to build a kite.

3. The box kite consists of a
   - ☐ a. nonrigid parachute-like design.
   - ☐ b. diamond-shaped model made of paper or cloth stretched on wooden sticks.
   - ☐ c. box decorated with designs.
   - ☐ d. rectangular box-shaped frame of wood with a wide band of cloth or paper at each end.

4. We can conclude from this section that most Americans prefer to fly a kite that is
   - ☐ a. flat.
   - ☐ b. bowed or angled.
   - ☐ c. nonrigid.
   - ☐ d. novelty.

5. The author explains the differences among the four kinds of kites through the use of
   - ☐ a. description.
   - ☐ b. analogy.
   - ☐ c. incident.
   - ☐ d. similarity.

6. For a kite to fly erratically it would have
   - ☐ a. to fly a straight course.
   - ☐ b. to loop and dive strangely.
   - ☐ c. to soar very high.
   - ☐ d. to rip in mid-flight.

CATEGORIES OF COMPREHENSION QUESTIONS

No 1: Subject Matter	No. 3: Supporting Details	No. 5: Clarifying Devices
No. 2: Main Idea	No. 4: Conclusion	No. 6: Vocabulary in Context

14. RIDING THE DESERT CAMEL

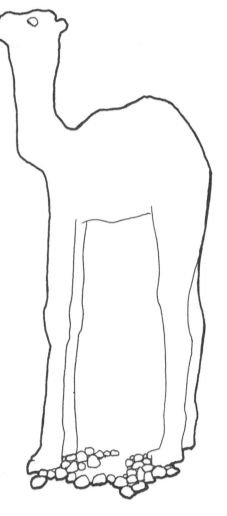

The back of a camel is too broad to let both of the rider's feet hang down—and there are no stirrups. The easiest way to ride, according to camel drivers, is to wrap one leg around the tall saddle horn and tuck the foot beneath the other leg which is allowed to dangle. You can also wrap both legs around the horn and sit Indian fashion, rest one or both legs on the camel's neck, ride sidesaddle, or even kneel back with the feet stuffed into the saddlebags. As for your hands, you can hold the reins gently, grasp a camel stick or clutch the saddle horn in desperation. But once you are accustomed to the camel's constant rocking gait, you can almost be lulled to sleep.

1. Choose the best title for this selection.
   - ☐ a. How to Ride a Camel
   - ☐ b. The Uncomfortable Camel
   - ☐ c. Riding in the Desert
   - ☐ d. Camel Drive

2. The author's main point is that riding a camel
   - ☐ a. demands patience.
   - ☐ b. is impossible.
   - ☐ c. requires ingenuity.
   - ☐ d. is dangerous.

3. According to the passage, which of the following statements is not true?
   - ☐ a. There are no stirrups to assist the camel rider.
   - ☐ b. Camels have a wider girth than horses.
   - ☐ c. Camels can be ridden sidesaddle.
   - ☐ d. The constant rocking of camels causes motion sickness.

4. We can conclude that the rider is supposed
   - ☐ a. to practice riding the animal.
   - ☐ b. to get used to the camel's gait.
   - ☐ c. to watch the camel drivers.
   - ☐ d. to find his most comfortable position.

5. The content of this paragraph can best be described as
   - ☐ a. argumentative.
   - ☐ b. descriptive.
   - ☐ c. critical.
   - ☐ d. instructive.

6. As used in the paragraph, lulled most nearly means
   - ☐ a. serenaded.
   - ☐ b. soothed.
   - ☐ c. shaken.
   - ☐ d. shocked.

CATEGORIES OF COMPREHENSION QUESTIONS

No. 1: Subject Matter	No. 3: Supporting Details	No. 5: Clarifying Devices
No. 2: Main Idea	No. 4: Conclusion	No. 6: Vocabulary in Context

15. CARRYING OIL

Not much is known about the cargo ship, *Elizabeth Watts.* She carried the world's first really substantial cargo of oil and arrived safely in England forty-five days later. Beyond that the records are blank—except to note that the ship's master had considerable difficulty in recruiting a crew. Sailors, not unreasonably, <u>balked</u> at signing on with a ship that was quite likely to explode and burn to the waterline halfway down the Delaware River. The master of the brig had to take drastic measures. He canvassed the inns, plied the sailors with grog and gently guided their staggering steps up the gangway. By the time they woke the ship was scudding into the Atlantic under full sail.

Today such tactics undoubtedly seem extreme. Yet they suggest the kind of problems that were to confront shipowners, as in the last half of the nineteenth century, they began, with considerable uneasiness, to cope with this new, unpredictable and often deadly cargo.

1. This passage is primarily about
   ☐ a. the *Elizabeth Watts.*
   ☐ b. difficulties of ships carrying oil.
   ☐ c. travels over the Atlantic.
   ☐ d. problems arising in some sailing cruises.

2. The main thought of this passage is
   ☐ a. early tankers used to explode and burn.
   ☐ b. with a cargo of oil, a shipowner faced several problems.
   ☐ c. oil is extremely explosive on the seas.
   ☐ d. people in general are afraid of oil.

3. According to the selection,
   ☐ a. the Delaware River was a dangerous area for ships to pass.
   ☐ b. the *Elizabeth Watts* carried the first good-sized cargo of oil.
   ☐ c. sailors today don't fear oil explosions.
   ☐ d. early sailors met their death on ships carrying oil as cargo.

4. After reading the passage, the reader may conclude that
   ☐ a. the *Elizabeth Watts* might have sailed in the late 1860s.
   ☐ b. the oil supply was limited because people would not work on ships.
   ☐ c. all shipowners had to be wicked people in order to get a crew.
   ☐ d. the average trip to England by boat takes forty-five days.

5. The author develops his main idea in the paragraph by using
   ☐ a. conversation and dialogue.
   ☐ b. an historical example.
   ☐ c. common problems of sailing.
   ☐ d. arguments and proof.

6. The best meaning of the word <u>balked</u> is
   ☐ a. discussed at length.
   ☐ b. stopped short, hesitated, or refused.
   ☐ c. fearful.
   ☐ d. extremely disgusted.

CATEGORIES OF COMPREHENSION QUESTIONS		
No. 1: Subject Matter	No. 3: Supporting Details	No. 5: Clarifying Devices
No. 2: Main Idea	No. 4: Conclusion	No. 6: Vocabulary in Context

16. THE FLYING PENGUIN

Penguins are better swimmers than many other totally aquatic creatures. This is a considerable feat for a bird which in distant ages past turned away from flight and took to the water to earn its living. Evolution moulded its wings into flippers and, as a bonus, equipped its body with built-in "shock absorbers."

After dining in the water, the penguin has a problem: how to get back aboard an ice floe some five or six feet above the water? The penguin swims in close, measures the distance with a watery eye and heads out some thirty feet. Then it turns and races at top speed under water, reaching possibly sixty miles per hour. Just short of the ice floe the penguin planes upwards and becomes a hurtling aerial torpedo. Most of the time, a penguin will make the edge of the ice floe. But on occasions it smacks hard into the side.

The impact would be hard enough to cripple the penguin or even kill it, were it not for its <u>ingenious</u> spring buffers. Penguin feathers grow straight out from the body and then towards their ends take a right-angled turn to make springy "shock absorbers."

1. This article is mainly about
   ☐ a. dangerous ice floes.
   ☐ b. the penguin as an aquatic creature.
   ☐ c. aquatic creatures of the ocean.
   ☐ d. the eating habits of the penguin.

2. Penguins are well-adapted to
   ☐ a. ice floes.
   ☐ b. aquatic life.
   ☐ c. flight.
   ☐ d. shock.

3. Penguins can swim
   ☐ a. up the side of an ice floe.
   ☐ b. as well as birds can fly.
   ☐ c. up to sixty miles per hour.
   ☐ d. because of their built-in shock absorbers.

4. We can infer from the article that penguins are
   ☐ a. often killed by hitting ice floes.
   ☐ b. able to measure distances underwater.
   ☐ c. similar to porpoises.
   ☐ d. protected from impacts by their feathers.

5. The author creates interest in his subject by using
   ☐ a. a great many facts.
   ☐ b. vivid description.
   ☐ c. precise argument.
   ☐ d. amusing narrative.

6. The word ingenious, as used in the passage, means
   ☐ a. clever.
   ☐ b. useful.
   ☐ c. candid.
   ☐ d. imitation.

CATEGORIES OF COMPREHENSION QUESTIONS

| No. 1: Subject Matter | No. 3: Supporting Details | No. 5: Clarifying Devices |
| No. 2: Main Idea | No. 4: Conclusion | No. 6: Vocabulary in Context |

17. THE GROUND HOG

The woodchuck is one of America's strangest animals. In a sense it is an animal known only to country people. A city man, not knowing the ways of wood-chucks, can walk through a far-mer's field and never see an army of as many as ten woodchucks silently watching him from scattered holes. To the <u>urban</u> eye, a woodchuck sitting ramrod-stiff by his hole, looks like a root, a clod of turf or a broken fence-post (if, indeed, he is noticed at all). But a farmer, following the city man, may clearly see woodchucks in all directions, watching like sentinels.

The chuck is a native American and is found in most states east of the Rockies and north to Alaska. He is hated by farmers. Why? An ordinary chuck eats a third of his weight in one day. (If you ate as much, you'd eat from 20 to 70 pounds a day, de-pending, of course, on your weight.) With this enormous appetite, a chuck eats about a half ton of alfalfa in a summer. Ten chucks in a big field would eat five tons! Besides this, chucks like nothing better than a morning snack of beanstalks from some-body's garden.

1. This article is mainly about the
   - ☐ a. problems of the American farmer.
   - ☐ b. hunting of the ground hog.
   - ☐ c. habits of the woodchuck.
   - ☐ d. difficulty of finding woodchucks.

2. Woodchucks live mainly
   - ☐ a. in Alaska.
   - ☐ b. on country turfs.
   - ☐ c. in urban areas.
   - ☐ d. on American farms.

3. To city dwellers, the woodchuck is
   - ☐ a. a big nuisance.
   - ☐ b. of great interest.
   - ☐ c. almost invisible.
   - ☐ d. a deterrent to country living.

4. The farmer considers the woodchuck
   - ☐ a. a useful, but misunderstood, animal.
   - ☐ b. undesirable because of his huge appetite.
   - ☐ c. useful in removing harmful vegetation.
   - ☐ d. a dangerous enemy to man.

5. To make his point, the author uses
   - ☐ a. an emotional appeal.
   - ☐ b. factual presentation.
   - ☐ c. biased opinion.
   - ☐ d. detailed comparison.

6. The word urban means
   - ☐ a. country.
   - ☐ b. city.
   - ☐ c. farm.
   - ☐ d. untrained.

CATEGORIES OF COMPREHENSION QUESTIONS

No. 1: Subject Matter	No. 3: Supporting Details	No. 5: Clarifying Devices
No. 2: Main Idea	No. 4: Conclusion	No. 6: Vocabulary in Context

18. ALL ABOUT EGGS

Birds' eggs come in a wide range of colors and markings. But, here again, there's almost certainly the hand of the great inventor, Nature, though we can't always discern the pattern. Sometimes, as in the case of the ground-nesting plover, the design is apparent; the plover's drab flecked egg blends so perfectly with the surroundings that only the keenest-eyed naturalist can ever find it. Once a man was told to look along a furrow in a ploughed paddock in which there were six plovers' nests. When he reached the end of the furrow he had walked on one nest and failed to spot the other five! Again, the eggs of the wild duck echo the green of the reeds amongst which she nests. The eggs of the red grouse, which are white or yellowish-white with blotches of reddish-brown or very dark brown, merge perfectly with the purple heather where she nests. It is the same with many other ground nesters.

Paradoxically, protection for the eggs of some birds comes from the bright, conspicuous coloring. Bold-colored eggs are often foul-tasting; a predator, such as a snake, cat, hedgehog, or mongoose has only to spit out a few repulsively flavored eggs before learning to associate the warning color with the unpleasant taste.

1. The best title for this passage is:
   ☐ a. Natural Camouflage of Eggs.
   ☐ b. A Wonder of an Egg.
   ☐ c. Nature's Course.
   ☐ d. A Variety of Eggs.

2. The main thought of the passage is that
   ☐ a. nature takes care of eggs.
   ☐ b. we can't always understand the pattern of eggs.
   ☐ c. eggs are well protected by parent birds.
   ☐ d. birds' eggs are colored to match the nests in which they hatch.

3. The eggs of the wild duck
   ☐ a. look like reeds.
   ☐ b. are a bright green.
   ☐ c. can easily crack.
   ☐ d. are the color of reeds in which they nest.

4. We can infer from the passage that
   ☐ a. the designs on some eggs serve to conceal.
   ☐ b. all eggs have a specific design.
   ☐ c. men are observant enough to notice eggs with designs.
   ☐ d. each pattern is unique with each egg.

5. The author develops his point by means of
   ☐ a. arguments and proof.
   ☐ b. comparison and contrast.
   ☐ c. citing cases.
   ☐ d. carefully chosen adjectives and adverbs.

6. As used in this passage, repulsively seems to mean
   ☐ a. deliciously.
   ☐ b. disgustingly.
   ☐ c. rottenly.
   ☐ d. ridiculously.

CATEGORIES OF COMPREHENSION QUESTIONS

No. 1: Subject Matter	No. 3: Supporting Details	No. 5: Clarifying Devices
No. 2: Main Idea	No. 4: Conclusion	No. 6: Vocabulary in Context

19. TEN THOUSAND YEARS OF THE BOW AND ARROW

Some modern bows are still made entirely of wood but most are constructed of various composites of wood, fiberglass, steel and plastic. Target bows require a pulling power of 20 to 60 pounds; hunting bows require 50 to 100 pounds. The old English rule was that a bow should be as tall as the man using it and his arrows half the length of the bow. Modern archers select their five- to six-foot bows to match their arrows, the length of which is based on the archer's "drawing length"—the distance between the base of the neck and the tip of the fingers. The arrows must be carefully crafted so that they do not "flirt"—swerve from a true flight line. Both wood and metal shafts are used, tipped with steel or brass, and feathered with tom turkey feathers or plastic.

Although new materials are used and although their appearance and power have been transformed many times over during their long, long history, the bow and arrow have stubbornly resisted obsolescence. Like the wheel or the lever and fulcrum, the basic idea of the bow and arrow was so practical—and simple—that it's highly unlikely that they will ever be relegated to dusty corners in museums. Many of man's brightest ideas become curiosity pieces once the world passes them by. With 10,000 years or more behind them, the bow and arrow are definitely not destined to be among them.

1. This passage focuses on the
   ☐ a. structure and long life of the bow and arrow.
   ☐ b. similarity between the bow and arrow.
   ☐ c. improvement of bows and arrows.
   ☐ d. design of the bow and arrow.

2. Although the bow and arrow have gone through frequent changes over time
   ☐ a. most of them are still made of wood.
   ☐ b. the basic idea behind them was so practical that they resisted extinction.
   ☐ c. their general use is still the same.
   ☐ d. the proportion of the size of the bow to the size of the arrow is still the same.

3. It is not true that
   ☐ a. hunting bows require a pulling power of 20 to 60 pounds.
   ☐ b. an old English rule specified that the arrow should be half the length the bow.
   ☐ c. in reference to arrows, "flirt" means to deviate from a direct flight.
   ☐ d. bows and arrows have been in use for at least ten thousand years.

4. The author feels that the use of the bow and arrow
   ☐ a. is similar to that of the wheel.
   ☐ b. will eventually fade away.
   ☐ c. has changed due to the archer's "drawing length".
   ☐ d. is not destined to end.

5. The author makes his points clear by using
   ☐ a. narration and dialogue.
   ☐ b. arguments and proof.
   ☐ c. comparison and contrast.
   ☐ d. description and explanation.

6. The word <u>obsolescence</u>, as used in this passage, means
   ☐ a. total destruction.
   ☐ b. going out of use.
   ☐ c. damage to internal parts.
   ☐ d. change over the years.

CATEGORIES OF COMPREHENSION QUESTIONS

No. 1: Subject Matter	No. 3: Supporting Details	No. 5: Clarifying Devices
No. 2: Main Idea	No. 4: Conclusion	No. 6: Vocabulary in Context

20. THE HONEYBEE

According to one entomologist, the queen bee develops to adulthood more rapidly than the worker. She emerges as a full-fledged queen after eight days of pupal change and sixteen days from the time when she was a tiny blue comma-shaped egg. The workers, on the other hand, require twenty-one days to complete the cycle from egg to adult, and the drones procrastinate until the twenty-fourth day to get on their brand-new legs and start ambling around for food.

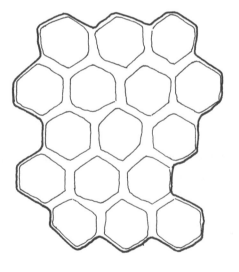

1. This passage is primarily about the
   □ a. adulthood of bees.
   □ b. amount of time bees remain as eggs.
   □ c. maturing of bees.
   □ d. queen bee and the worker bee.

2. The only difference mentioned between the queen bee and worker bees is
   □ a. that the workers are stronger.
   □ b. that the queen bee works less.
   □ c. in their life expectancies.
   □ d. in the time necessary for maturing.

3. The author says that
   □ a. drones take twenty-eight days to become adults.
   □ b. it takes eight days for a full-fledged queen to develop.
   □ c. the king, queen, drone and worker are the only types.
   □ d. the queen develops more rapidly than the worker.

4. According to the passage, it appears that bees
   □ a. vary in maturity rate according to their type.
   □ b. have a high maturity rate.
   □ c. can live a long time after fully maturing.
   □ d. have a high mortality rate.

5. In developing his point, the author makes use of
   □ a. scientific theories.
   □ b. common sense.
   □ c. scientific arguments.
   □ d. the observation of a specialist.

6. An entomologist is a person who
   □ a. studies the life cycle of bees.
   □ b. raises honeybees.
   □ c. studies insects.
   □ d. collects honeybees.

CATEGORIES OF COMPREHENSION QUESTIONS		
No. 1: Subject Matter	No. 3: Supporting Details	No. 5: Clarifying Devices
No. 2: Main Idea	No. 4: Conclusion	No. 6: Vocabulary in Context

21. THE CRUSADES

From a military point of view, the Crusades must be written off as a failure for the West. After changing hands so many times, the Christian kingdom of Jerusalem was finally taken back by the Moslems. But during the nearly two hundred years of fighting between East and West, it is plain now that each side made major contributions to the culture of the other. That interchange let in a few rays of light over a darkened Europe and removed for all time the wall of ignorance that had always existed between Europe and Asia.

1. The best title for this selection would be:
   ☐ a. Conquest of the Middle East.
   ☐ b. Defeat of the Crusaders.
   ☐ c. Outcome of the Crusades.
   ☐ d. Treasures of the East.

2. The most outstanding result of the Crusades was that the Moslems and Crusaders
   ☐ a. became bitter enemies.
   ☐ b. exchanged knowledge.
   ☐ c. divided the kingdom of Jerusalem.
   ☐ d. reached a peace agreement.

3. The number of years that the Crusades lasted is
   ☐ a. ten.
   ☐ b. fifty.
   ☐ c. one hundred.
   ☐ d. two hundred.

4. The achievements of the Crusades as compared with its aims were
   ☐ a. quite different.
   ☐ b. greater than expected.
   ☐ c. similar.
   ☐ d. much more realistic.

5. The "wall of ignorance" between Europe and Asia is a metaphor for the
   ☐ a. darkness that enveloped Europe.
   ☐ b. pointless fighting between the two.
   ☐ c. misconceptions on both sides.
   ☐ d. Jerusalem wall which prevented European influence.

6. The best synonym for interchange as it is used in this passage is
   ☐ a. compromise of principles.
   ☐ b. change of occupation of Jerusalem.
   ☐ c. battle strategy.
   ☐ d. sharing of information.

CATEGORIES OF COMPREHENSION QUESTIONS

No. 1: Subject Matter	No. 3: Supporting Details	No. 5: Clarifying Devices
No. 2: Main Idea	No. 4: Conclusion	No. 6: Vocabulary in Context

22. DIAMONDS

The quality of a diamond and the skilled workmanship needed to enhance it figure heavily in the stone's worth. Color, freedom from flaws, weight and cutting are the hallmarks. Diamonds can be yellow or black, red, pink, blue, brown, or green; but pure white, which will refract a shower of hues when properly cut, is the most desirable color. Flawless, when applied to diamonds, has a very special meaning. If a trained eye using ten-power magnification in normal daylight detects no flaws, cracks, carbon spots or other blemishes, the stone is considered flawless.

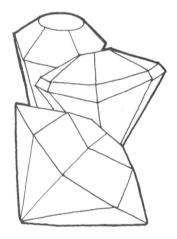

1. This paragraph is mainly about the diamond's value as determined by the
   - ☐ a. amount of skilled workmanship used on it.
   - ☐ b. quality of the stone.
   - ☐ c. intricacy of its setting.
   - ☐ d. number of carats it weighs.

2. Two hallmarks of quality in a diamond discussed in this paragraph are
   - ☐ a. weight and size.
   - ☐ b. cutting and polishing.
   - ☐ c. setting and finishing.
   - ☐ d. color and freedom from flaws.

3. A flawless stone is one that shows no flaws, cracks, carbon spots, or other blemishes in normal daylight under a magnification power of
   - ☐ a. five.
   - ☐ b. ten.
   - ☐ c. fifteen.
   - ☐ d. twenty.

4. A diamond's worth is enhanced not only by its weight and expert cutting, but also by its
   - ☐ a. color and flawlessness.
   - ☐ b. market price.
   - ☐ c. historical significance.
   - ☐ d. symbolic value.

5. The author shows which qualities of diamonds are valued through
   - ☐ a. an explanation of colors and terms.
   - ☐ b. an imaginative description.
   - ☐ c. anecdotal references.
   - ☐ d. romantic imagery.

6. The word blemishes, as used in the passage, means
   - ☐ a. dark spots.
   - ☐ b. defects.
   - ☐ c. cracks.
   - ☐ d. small blisters.

CATEGORIES OF COMPREHENSION QUESTIONS

No. 1: Subject Matter	No. 3: Supporting Details	No. 5: Clarifying Devices
No. 2: Main Idea	No. 4: Conclusion	No. 6: Vocabulary in Context

23. THE BIRTH OF THE WHEEL

Fragments of ancient cultures indicate that the wheel was probably developed in logical steps. From rollers or logs, which were very likely the first wheel-like devices, solid wheels evolved, which were little more than chunks of round tree trunks on a fixed axle. After centuries of bumping and wobbling on the massive, solid wheels, hub and spokes were introduced, making it possible to construct wheels in sections. As wheels turned faster, they wore faster and became lopsided. Metal came into common use to sheath the axle from the grinding wear of wheel action. Then "tires" of wood or copper were devised to stand up better under the rigors of travel.

1. The best title for this selection would be:
   - □ a. The Invention of the Tire.
   - □ b. The Development of the Wheel.
   - □ c. Early Uses of the Wheel.
   - □ d. The Advantages of Copper Wheels.

2. As time passed, wheels became
   - □ a. lighter and less durable.
   - □ b. faster and heavier.
   - □ c. stronger and lighter.
   - □ d. heavier and more durable.

3. The development from the first wheel-like devices to the copper wheel occurred over
   - □ a. several centuries.
   - □ b. one hundred years.
   - □ c. fifty years.
   - □ d. one century.

4. Metal began to be used on the axles because it
   - □ a. was flexible.
   - □ b. wore longer.
   - □ c. was easier to work with.
   - □ d. was readily available.

5. The author stresses the logical steps in the development of the wheel by
   - □ a. listing improvements in their order of occurrence.
   - □ b. listing first the problems then the solutions.
   - □ c. emphasizing only the improvements.
   - □ d. using arguments to support his case.

6. The best synonym for lopsided would be
   - □ a. curved.
   - □ b. straight.
   - □ c. unbalanced.
   - □ d. bent.

CATEGORIES OF COMPREHENSION QUESTIONS

No. 1: Subject Matter	No. 3: Supporting Details	No. 5: Clarifying Devices
No. 2: Main Idea	No. 4: Conclusion	No. 6: Vocabulary in Context

24. CREATURES OF THE DRY WORLD

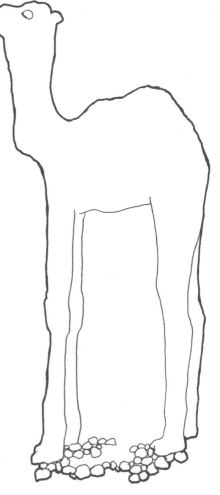

The popular belief that camels store water in their humps is correct in substance: water is indeed stored there but in the form of fat. On long, waterless marches the camel draws on this reserve (as well as on the water stored in three special reservoir compartments in its stomach) by making metabolic water.

Anyone who has seen fat spluttering in a pan has seen the process: the spluttering is caused by water escaping from the fat in the form of steam bubbles. Something of the same sort occurs inside the body of the camel and some other desert creatures. Water is <u>released</u> by the breaking down of sugars and other carbohydrates or by the oxidation of the hydrogen or carbon.

1. The best title for this selection would be:
   ☐ a. Desert Survival Techniques.
   ☐ b. Making Metabolic Water.
   ☐ c. The Camel's Water Storage Methods.
   ☐ d. The Camel: Rugged Beast of Burden.

2. The fat in the camel's hump is used for
   ☐ a. protection against cold.
   ☐ b. protection against heat.
   ☐ c. production of energy.
   ☐ d. storage of water.

3. In which part of the body does the camel store water in the usual form?
   ☐ a. Hump
   ☐ b. Liver
   ☐ c. Stomach
   ☐ d. Tail

4. The author suggests that water can be released from fat by the breakdown of
   ☐ a. carbon.
   ☐ b. oxygen.
   ☐ c. carbohydrates.
   ☐ d. hydrogen.

5. The author mentions the spluttering of fat to show that
   ☐ a. the camel uses desert heat to melt fat.
   ☐ b. heated water turns to steam.
   ☐ c. oxidation of hydrocarbons yields water.
   ☐ d. water can be stored in fat.

6. The word <u>released</u>, as used in this selection, means
   ☐ a. is freed.
   ☐ b. is produced.
   ☐ c. is expelled.
   ☐ d. is transferred.

CATEGORIES OF COMPREHENSION QUESTIONS		
No. 1: Subject Matter	No. 3: Supporting Details	No. 5: Clarifying Devices
No. 2: Main Idea	No. 4: Conclusion	No. 6: Vocabulary in Context

25. SMASHING THROUGH THE NORTHWEST PASSAGE

The northward transit up the Prince of Wales Strait was easily accomplished. There followed a month of intensive ice testing in Viscount Melville Sound to determine just how well the *Manhattan* could <u>comport</u> herself in varying ice conditions. Ice scientists climbed out onto test floes and drilled them for thickness and cored them for samples. The ship was then driven through the floes at varying speeds to establish a relationship between the physical properties of the ice and the horsepower required to break through it. This was hard, slugging work with little to relieve the monotony for those not actively engaged. But the test data collected was a crucial reason for the voyage.

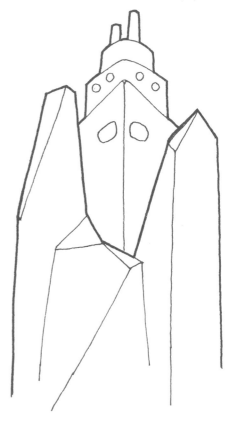

1. This passage is about
   ☐ a. sailing on the high seas.
   ☐ b. shipping in bad weather.
   ☐ c. the frozen Arctic.
   ☐ d. navigating in frozen waters.

2. What is the main idea of this passage?
   ☐ a. Identifying ice conditions in the Arctic
   ☐ b. Sailing up the Prince of Wales Strait
   ☐ c. Testing problems of navigating icy waters
   ☐ d. Measuring the length of the Northwest Passage

3. What was the purpose of driving the ship through the ice floes at various speeds?
   ☐ a. To test for quality of ice
   ☐ b. To determine the most effective speed for different types of ice
   ☐ c. To compare the size of the ice to the size of the ship
   ☐ d. To see how fast they could get through

4. The passage suggests that because of the testing, future sailors may be
   ☐ a. more experienced.
   ☐ b. more knowledgeable.
   ☐ c. less foolhardy.
   ☐ d. inconvenienced.

5. The purpose of the passage is
   ☐ a. to acquaint the reader with what the *Manhattan* had done.
   ☐ b. to persuade the reader of the importance of the *Manhattan's* voyage.
   ☐ c. to identify the uses of ships.
   ☐ d. to explain the difficulties of sailing in icy waters.

6. In examining how well the *Manhattan* could comport herself, the scientists investigated the ship's
   ☐ a. resistance.
   ☐ b. conduct.
   ☐ c. acceleration.
   ☐ d. passage.

CATEGORIES OF COMPREHENSION QUESTIONS		
No. 1: Subject Matter	No. 3: Supporting Details	No. 5: Clarifying Devices
No. 2: Main Idea	No. 4: Conclusion	No. 6: Vocabulary in Context

26. COLLEGE DAYS IN COLONIAL TIMES

A college freshman in colonial times could never wear his hat in the Yard (campus), except in snow, hail or rain, or unless both hands were full. Whenever a freshman's hands were full, it was probably with food and drink for some upperclassman, for he was obliged to serve as errand boy to any sophomore, junior, senior, graduate student or tutor who might choose to give him an order. At their command, he hurried from the buttery with breakfasts of bread and beer (eaten in student rooms); he carried notes, fetched tobacco, took wigs to be curled, and clothes to be pressed. He had to accept every command with re-spect—no saucy backtalk, no laughter. A rebellious lad could expect quick punishment.

1. This paragraph is primarily about
   - ☐ a. freshmen serving upperclassmen.
   - ☐ b. the upperclassmen's harsh treatment of freshmen.
   - ☐ c. the code of manners on campuses.
   - ☐ d. freshmen respect for upperclassmen.

2. The behavior of the college freshmen had to be
   - ☐ a. rebellious.
   - ☐ b. clumsy.
   - ☐ c. humble.
   - ☐ d. unforgettable.

3. A freshman could not wear his hat on campus unless
   - ☐ a. he were in the company of other freshmen.
   - ☐ b. he were running an errand.
   - ☐ c. the weather were very bad.
   - ☐ d. an upperclassman gave permission.

4. The freshman described in the paragraph
   - ☐ a. attended a strict military school.
   - ☐ b. was very poor.
   - ☐ c. was at an Ivy League school.
   - ☐ d. existed in the past.

5. The author develops his main idea in this paragraph through the use of
   - ☐ a. vivid description.
   - ☐ b. a historical account.
   - ☐ c. negative arguments.
   - ☐ d. comparison and contrast.

6. The word obliged is closest in meaning to
   - ☐ a. required.
   - ☐ b. forced.
   - ☐ c. willing.
   - ☐ d. quick.

CATEGORIES OF COMPREHENSION QUESTIONS

| No. 1: Subject Matter | No. 3: Supporting Details | No. 5: Clarifying Devices |
| No. 2: Main Idea | No. 4: Conclusion | No. 6: Vocabulary in Context |

27. MUSIC IN THE STREETS

In a large office building on an Amsterdam street, the windows are open. About midmorning, when it's time to stretch and catch an extra breath of invigorating air, a young secretary goes to a window, leans far out and throws something to an up-raised hand below. After the paper is uncrinkled and its list of tunes noted, the man who caught it pockets a handful of coins. For the next quarter-hour the fine spring morning becomes even finer as the air is filled with the rich, resonant music of the street organ. More smiling faces appear at the office windows. Even the boss smiles and takes a break, for he, too, has an invest-ment in a favorite tune. One of the coins the secretary threw down was his.

1. This passage could best be titled:
   - ☐ a. Dutch Treat.
   - ☐ b. Organic Music.
   - ☐ c. Amsterdam's Street Musicians.
   - ☐ d. The Midmorning Grind.

2. The street musicians
   - ☐ a. are considered public nuisances.
   - ☐ b. are responsible for "loafing" on the job.
   - ☐ c. will play anything for enough money.
   - ☐ d. help make the workday more pleasant.

3. The street musicians
   - ☐ a. will play only for young secretaries.
   - ☐ b. are often bribed to leave.
   - ☐ c. are employed in office buildings.
   - ☐ d. will play requests for money.

4. Street organ music
   - ☐ a. is a pleasant Dutch custom.
   - ☐ b. is of no use to anyone.
   - ☐ c. is stopped if the boss's tune isn't played.
   - ☐ d. should be prohibited in public.

5. The author uses
   - ☐ a. contrast and comparison.
   - ☐ b. description.
   - ☐ c. conversation.
   - ☐ d. arguments.

6. The word <u>invigorating</u>, as used in the passage, seems to mean
   - ☐ a. intoxicating.
   - ☐ b. noxious.
   - ☐ c. energy-giving.
   - ☐ d. pleasant-smelling.

CATEGORIES OF COMPREHENSION QUESTIONS

No. 1: Subject Matter	No. 3: Supporting Details	No. 5: Clarifying Devices
No. 2: Main Idea	No. 4: Conclusion	No. 6: Vocabulary in Context

28. THEY DIG HISTORY

The modern archaeologist must exercise extreme care when digging around ancient ruins. Further, for effective research, he needs a background knowledge of languages, natural science, and the cultures of different peoples. For these reasons, one-man expeditions are a thing of the past. Now, when an expedition arrives at the site of an ancient city, the archaeologist leads a party of experts in anthropology, geology, geography and other sciences. Members of the party must know surveying, photography, drafting, and mechanical repair. And even with all the <u>accumulated</u> knowledge represented by the experts at the dig, final reports on important finds must still wait until opinions have been heard from specialists in museums and universities scattered around the world.

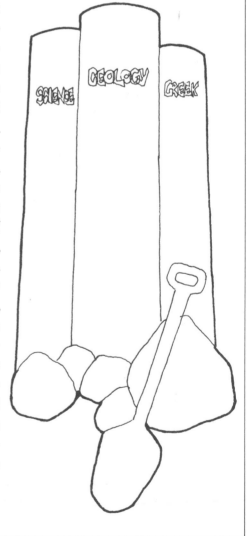

1. The best title for this passage is:
   - ☐ a. One-Man Dig.
   - ☐ b. The Archaeological Team.
   - ☐ c. Archaeologists in Ancient Ruins.
   - ☐ d. Follow the Leader.

2. The main idea of the passage is that
   - ☐ a. most professionals work together today.
   - ☐ b. archaeologists have limited knowledge.
   - ☐ c. there is more to archaeology than just digging.
   - ☐ d. archaeological research requires expert assistance.

3. According to the passage, archaeologists
   - ☐ a. rely on the opinions of specialists at universities and museums on important finds.
   - ☐ b. must also be specialists in anthropology, geology, and geography.
   - ☐ c. relate their work to all other sciences.
   - ☐ d. prefer working alone.

4. The modern archaeologist can no longer conduct one-man expeditions because
   - ☐ a. his work requires the aid of others.
   - ☐ b. he is no longer the leader of expeditions.
   - ☐ c. he is willing to share his work.
   - ☐ d. he needs others to help with the heavy work.

5. This passage could be labeled
   - ☐ a. factual.
   - ☐ b. humorous.
   - ☐ c. controversial.
   - ☐ d. theoretical.

6. The word, <u>accumulated</u>, as used in this passage, means
   - ☐ a. practical.
   - ☐ b. substantial.
   - ☐ c. diverse.
   - ☐ d. collected.

CATEGORIES OF COMPREHENSION QUESTIONS

No. 1: Subject Matter	No. 3: Supporting Details	No. 5: Clarifying Devices
No. 2: Main Idea	No. 4: Conclusion	No. 6: Vocabulary in Context

29. SHORE-TO-SHORE SHUTTLE

At every traveled crossing of streams too wide to jump and too deep to ford, ferryboats once did the work of bridges. Even today if you travel by road or rail, strategic traffic routes around the world bring you to waters where bridges and tunnels can't reach or won't pay, and where the only dry crossing is a ferry ride. But a lengthening list of abandoned runs leaves no doubt that the use of the ferryboat is declining.

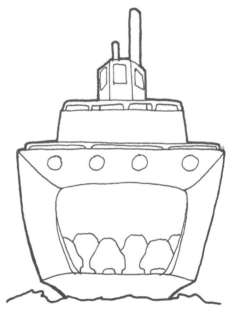

Like West Virginia's Harpers Ferry or the former Harris's Ferry, now Pennsylvania's Harrisburg, many ferries remain in name only. A few ferries have quit in the red, their traffic and profits dried up by alternate routes. Most ferries, however, sailed to prosperous ends. Overwhelmed by lines of backed-up traffic, they gave way to bridges.

1. This story could best be titled:
   - ☐ a. Bridge to the Past.
   - ☐ b. The Vanishing Ferry.
   - ☐ c. The Lonesome Ferry.
   - ☐ d. Prosperous Ends.

2. The relationship between the ferry and the bridge is similar to the relationship between the
   - ☐ a. horse-and-buggy and the car.
   - ☐ b. child and the adult.
   - ☐ c. train and the rocket.
   - ☐ d. bridge and the steamship.

3. Many ferry runs have stopped because
   - ☐ a. they lost money due to inflation.
   - ☐ b. they have become prohibitively expensive.
   - ☐ c. many important rivers of the past have lost their importance.
   - ☐ d. they could not handle the capacity that a bridge could.

4. The fate of the ferry indicates that
   - ☐ a. competition is always fair.
   - ☐ b. the bridge will soon suffer a similar fate.
   - ☐ c. progress often means the end of tradition.
   - ☐ d. the unemployment of many ferry pilots will be harmful to the economy.

5. Harpers Ferry is mentioned
   - ☐ a. only to serve as an example of expiring ferries.
   - ☐ b. to indicate the author's sentimentality.
   - ☐ c. because it is one of the focal points of the passage.
   - ☐ d. to make the reader nostalgic.

6. To quit in the red means to quit
   - ☐ a. bravely.
   - ☐ b. in debt.
   - ☐ c. unhappily.
   - ☐ d. prosperously.

CATEGORIES OF COMPREHENSION QUESTIONS

| No. 1: Subject Matter | No. 3: Supporting Details | No. 5: Clarifying Devices |
| No. 2: Main Idea | No. 4: Conclusion | No. 6: Vocabulary in Context |

30. SHELLS FROM THE SEA

Sea shells are actually external skeletons which have kept their color and luster long after the death of the tenant. They are the hard coverings of a marine animal known as the mollusk. This casing, which protects its soft, defenseless body from predatory sea dwellers, is made up largely of carbonate of lime and is often stone-hard.

Shells usually have three layers. The outer covering of horny skin forms the protective surface. The middle and thickest layer is made up of prisms and governs the color pattern of the shell. Innermost is the smooth, shining nacreous lining often called mother-of-pearl. From this delicate surface, which gleams blue, rose, green and other pastel shades, is taken the material for pearl buttons, jewelry and adornments.

1. This passage describes mostly
   □ a. the way shells are formed and what they look like.
   □ b. the many varieties of shells.
   □ c. the commercial uses of shells and mother-of-pearl.
   □ d. the historical significance of shells.

2. Shells are best described as
   □ a. beautiful three-layered skeletons of sea animals.
   □ b. carbonate of lime rocks found on the ocean floor.
   □ c. delicate remains of withered marine life.
   □ d. gleaming gem-like wastes called mother-of-pearl.

3. The middle layer of the shell determines its
   □ a. length and size.
   □ b. weight and thickness.
   □ c. color pattern.
   □ d. surface texture.

4. The beauty of shells is a
   □ a. commercial creation.
   □ b. natural phenomenon.
   □ c. result of sea deposits.
   □ d. form of protective coloration.

5. The author develops his point by means of
   □ a. narration.
   □ b. definition.
   □ c. comparison.
   □ d. description.

6. A predatory sea dweller is one that
   □ a. lives in harmony with other sea animals.
   □ b. preys on other sea animals.
   □ c. grows its own shell.
   □ d. is brightly colored.

CATEGORIES OF COMPREHENSION QUESTIONS		
No. 1: Subject Matter	No. 3: Supporting Details	No. 5: Clarifying Devices
No. 2: Main Idea	No. 4: Conclusion	No. 6: Vocabulary in Context

31. THE SUBJECT OF SNEEZES

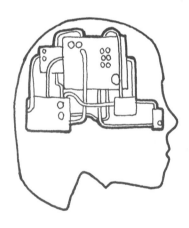

The simple sneeze is actually a complex reaction. The impulse to sneeze, scientifically known as a protective reflex, comes from irritation of a group of nerves back of the eyes. When the signals reach the brain, the body takes a quick breath, muscles contract violently, and "kerchoo" comes out. Sometimes a sneeze can be stopped by pressing on the bridge of the nose, at the point where the bone ends. There's a tiny nerve there that signals the brain to stop the sneeze, but nobody knows exactly how it works. The odd combination of a breeze and a bright light can also cause sneezing. A skeptical veterinarian once set out to disprove this. He deliberately stood on the beach at Cape Cod in a brisk breeze and stared at the sun's reflection on the water. Sure enough, he started sneezing. Not only that, but his dog did too.

1. The best title for this passage is:
   - □ a. Coughing with a Kick.
   - □ b. Explanation of a Sneeze.
   - □ c. A Skeptic Blows His Theory.
   - □ d. The Winds of Cape Cod.

2. This passage
   - □ a. describes the beauty of Cape Cod.
   - □ b. shows the foolishness of skeptical veterinarians.
   - □ c. explores the cause of a sneeze.
   - □ d. explains the effect of bright light on the protective reflex.

3. Sneezes
   - □ a. result from the contraction of muscles.
   - □ b. are more harmful to dogs than humans.
   - □ c. can be stopped by pressure on the nose.
   - □ d. are hereditary impulses.

4. The article shows that a sneeze can
   - □ a. be a symptom of a disease.
   - □ b. protect the body from damage.
   - □ c. occur more often at the beach.
   - □ d. result from various stimuli.

5. The author, in discussing sneezes, uses
   - □ a. scientific fact.
   - □ b. folklore.
   - □ c. arguments and proof.
   - □ d. unfounded rumor.

6. The word skeptical is closest in meaning to
   - □ a. renowned.
   - □ b. typical.
   - □ c. doubting.
   - □ d. obscure.

CATEGORIES OF COMPREHENSION QUESTIONS		
No. 1: Subject Matter	No. 3: Supporting Details	No. 5: Clarifying Devices
No. 2: Main Idea	No. 4: Conclusion	No. 6: Vocabulary in Context

32. LIZARD OF THE DESERT

The dabb, a big lizard of eastern Saudi Arabia, is a two-foot-long, heavy-bodied creature with a spine-covered tail. Living in deep burrows often seen in hard, gravelly terrain, the dabb is edible with meat resembling tough lamb. Desert dabb fanciers, who now drive pickup trucks instead of camels, sometimes capture them by extending a hose from their car's exhaust pipe into the burrow. The groggy lizard soon staggers out and is easily captured. A cornered dabb puts on a ferocious display, with much hissing and puffing, and his thrashing tail can inflict painful bruises. But generally he is a fraud; if careful, you can capture him by hand. The dabb is primarily a vegetarian. Its body color varies from slate-gray to bright yellow—according to changes in temperature apparently—and it is capable of sprinting almost as fast as a man can run.

1. This passage focuses on the
   - ☐ a. desert dabb hunters.
   - ☐ b. spiny-tailed desert creature.
   - ☐ c. mating habits of the dabb.
   - ☐ d. burrowing of dabbs.

2. The dabb is
   - ☐ a. a large, fairly harmless lizard.
   - ☐ b. small enough to be held in the hand.
   - ☐ c. eaten in Arabia in preference to lamb.
   - ☐ d. extremely dangerous when cornered.

3. Some people capture dabbs by making them
   - ☐ a. groggy from hissing and puffing.
   - ☐ b. run into a dabb-trap.
   - ☐ c. breathe exhaust fumes.
   - ☐ d. sprint until exhausted.

4. The dabb may avoid capture
   - ☐ a. by escaping to his deep burrow.
   - ☐ b. because he is so ferocious.
   - ☐ c. by sprinting as fast as the captor can run.
   - ☐ d. by changing his color.

5. The author uses
   - ☐ a. hearsay.
   - ☐ b. factual description.
   - ☐ c. contrast.
   - ☐ d. arguments and proof.

6. A fraud is a
   - ☐ a. toad.
   - ☐ b. coward.
   - ☐ c. terror.
   - ☐ d. fake.

CATEGORIES OF COMPREHENSION QUESTIONS

No. 1: Subject Matter	No. 3: Supporting Details	No. 5: Clarifying Devices
No. 2: Main Idea	No. 4: Conclusion	No. 6: Vocabulary in Context

33. A TOUCH OF RIBBON

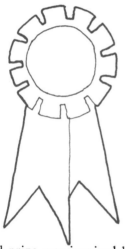

Awards seem to demand ribbon. All manner of diplomas and prizes—from the Bachelor of Arts sheepskin to Best in Show ribbon—are decorated with a crisp swirl of color, usually blue or red.

The giving of a blue ribbon for first prize originated with the English knights. The highest order of knighthood, the Order of the Garter, was represented by a wide sash of blue. A red ribbon for second prize was inspired by the second order of knighthood, the Order of the Bath, represented by a crimson sash.

Knighthood was not passed from father to son, but had to be earned. The Order of the Garter led a long list of honors which could be <u>bestowed</u> upon a deserving subject. From the awarding of orders of knighthood—and the attendant sashes, badges, and medallions—came the idea of military decorations for valor and the distinctive ribbons which represent them.

1. This passage deals with the
   ☐ a. importance of ribbon.
   ☐ b. significance of knighthood.
   ☐ c. relationship of ribbon to award.
   ☐ d. educational merits of ribbons.

2. The ceremonious use of ribbon
   ☐ a. is becoming obsolete.
   ☐ b. has been adopted by many types of organizations.
   ☐ c. is unfounded by common sense.
   ☐ d. reflects man's passion for material rewards.

3. The Order of the Garter
   ☐ a. used a wide, crimson sash.
   ☐ b. was decorated with a crisp swirl of color.
   ☐ c. was an inherited honor.
   ☐ d. was higher than the Order of the Bath.

4. From the popularity of ceremonious ribbons, it can be concluded that
   ☐ a. a ribbon is often a symbol of an award made.
   ☐ b. ribbons are cheaper to manufacture than medallions.
   ☐ c. the use of ceremonious ribbons appeals only to the simple mind.
   ☐ d. ribbons are more interesting than medals because they are brighter.

5. The author discusses knighthood in order
   ☐ a. to emphasize the relationship between knighthood and the military.
   ☐ b. to give an historical perspective on ribbons.
   ☐ c. to show that knighthood served a valuable function.
   ☐ d. to demonstrate the fact that ribbon is crucial to all ceremony.

6. Something which is <u>bestowed</u> upon someone is
   ☐ a. sold to him.
   ☐ b. lent to him.
   ☐ c. awarded to him.
   ☐ d. denied him temporarily.

CATEGORIES OF COMPREHENSION QUESTIONS

No. 1: Subject Matter	No. 3: Supporting Details	No. 5: Clarifying Devices
No. 2: Main Idea	No. 4: Conclusion	No. 6: Vocabulary in Context

34. SCRIBES

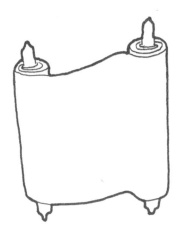

Scribes or writers were first employed by the military officers in ancient Egypt to record the names of recruits. Later, in Hebrew times, scribes progressed from mere copyists into interpreters and teachers of the law. During the great ages of Islam they kept alive not only the Holy Koran, but also the irreplaceable writings of the Greeks and Romans. In the Dark Ages and the Middle Ages of Europe writers preserved most of man's accumulated knowledge. So important was their role that Arab poets <u>accorded</u> the pen equal rank with the sword. Writing was a noble and essential skill and men who knew how to write were honored and valued. Even the invention of the printing press did not entirely displace writing. Although books became more common, the ability to write them and read them did not. It is only in this century, with the growth of public education, that the need for scribes dwindled.

1. This passage treats the
   □ a. characteristics of scribes.
   □ b. social standing allotted the scribe.
   □ c. system of public-school education.
   □ d. historical development of the duty of scribes.

2. Scribes were highly valued before this century because
   □ a. they were generally from wealthy families.
   □ b. few people could read and write.
   □ c. good scribes were usually good fighters as well.
   □ d. they were very kind and generous.

3. One thing not mentioned as one of the jobs of a scribe at one time or other is
   □ a. teaching law.
   □ b. rewriting words of Greeks and Romans.
   □ c. translating from Hebrew to Arabic.
   □ d. recording names of army recruits.

4. The status of the scribe declined with the advance of public education because
   □ a. the role of the scribe could now be handled by the people themselves.
   □ b. scribes became the teachers of the public schools.
   □ c. scribes lost interest in their jobs.
   □ d. the scribes died out due to old age.

5. In discussing the role of the scribe, the author arranges his information
   □ a. in order of importance.
   □ b. in order of interest.
   □ c. in order of use.
   □ d. in order of time.

6. The word <u>accorded</u>, as used in the passage, means
   □ a. superimposed.
   □ b. granted.
   □ c. insisted.
   □ d. written about.

CATEGORIES OF COMPREHENSION QUESTIONS

| No. 1: Subject Matter | No. 3: Supporting Details | No. 5: Clarifying Devices |
| No. 2: Main Idea | No. 4: Conclusion | No. 6: Vocabulary in Context |

35. KNIVES, FORKS AND SPOONS

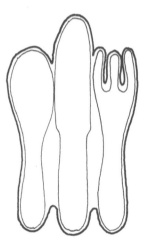

Nobody knows for sure, but the knife is probably far older than either the fork or spoon. Some authorities say the knife was invented not by man but by higher forms of apes, who are believed to have used stones for tearing long before man's time. Man was making and using stone knives 45,000 years ago. Authorities believe that he held chunks of meat in his mouth, slicing off what he didn't want to swallow. This style of eating continued through the Middle Ages in Europe, with man using his hunting knife or fighting dagger to separate himself from his steak.

Because guests used to bring pointed knives to dinner, King Louis XIV of France nervously issued an <u>edict</u> against them in 1700. The round-ended knife, like the one in use today, then became popular. Although these had already been in limited use for 250 years, many had wide flat ends and were almost like spoons.

1. This article could best be titled:
   - ☐ a. Cutting Remarks.
   - ☐ b. Get to the Point.
   - ☐ c. The Oldest Utensil.
   - ☐ d. Mack the Knife.

2. Knives
   - ☐ a. were first made in America.
   - ☐ b. haven't always been pointed.
   - ☐ c. were feared by Louis XIV.
   - ☐ d. have a long history of use.

3. Man, up through the Middle Ages,
   - ☐ a. used the same knife for hunting and eating.
   - ☐ b. had developed only the round-ended knife.
   - ☐ c. carved his meat inside his mouth.
   - ☐ d. preferred stone knives for eating.

4. An edict issued by Louis XIV of France led to
   - ☐ a. more refined European eating habits.
   - ☐ b. the development of the round-ended knife.
   - ☐ c. a greater reliance on the fork.
   - ☐ d. the popularity of steaks at supper.

5. The author uses
   - ☐ a. wit.
   - ☐ b. insights.
   - ☐ c. observation.
   - ☐ d. description.

6. An edict seems to be a
   - ☐ a. judge's decision.
   - ☐ b. business regulation.
   - ☐ c. royal order.
   - ☐ d. rule of etiquette.

CATEGORIES OF COMPREHENSION QUESTIONS

| No. 1: Subject Matter | No. 3: Supporting Details | No. 5: Clarifying Devices |
| No. 2: Main Idea | No. 4: Conclusion | No. 6: Vocabulary in Context |

36. CORAL DWELLERS

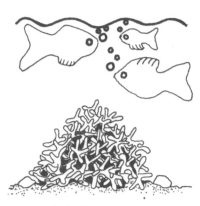

Living in the shelter of the reefs, in the quiet haven of coral forests beneath the wind-blown surface, countless varieties of brilliantly colored, almost fluorescent coral fish swim lazily through the branches. Among the loveliest are the bizarre "angel" or "butterfly" fish. Their Latin name means "bristle-toothed." Angel fish have a long, trunk-shaped mouth which enables them to pick up their food from the coral. They are not very good swimmers but luckily, like most brightly colored coral fish, they do not taste good either, so few carnivorous species ever harm them. They have practically no enemies, in fact, except members of their own species who sometimes try to penetrate their living areas. For a long time the fantastic colors and designs of these fishes were a riddle to scientists, but today the glowing dots and stripes are believed to be a kind of signal to warn others of the species away from their living areas.

1. The best title for this paragraph is:
   - ☐ a. Fish and How They Live.
   - ☐ b. The Bristle Tooth Fish.
   - ☐ c. Survival of the Fittest.
   - ☐ d. The Reef Shelter.

2. The main idea of the paragraph is that angel fish are
   - ☐ a. protected by nature's safety measures.
   - ☐ b. lonely and colorful.
   - ☐ c. poor swimmers.
   - ☐ d. a riddle to scientists.

3. Most of the angel fish's enemies are
   - ☐ a. larger fish.
   - ☐ b. carnivorous species.
   - ☐ c. fast swimmers.
   - ☐ d. other angel fish.

4. Scientists probably were interested in the angel fish due to its
   - ☐ a. abundance.
   - ☐ b. elephant-like appearance.
   - ☐ c. colorful characteristics.
   - ☐ d. lack of enemies.

5. The author speaks of angel fish as
   - ☐ a. a contrast to other colorful fish.
   - ☐ b. the strongest of coral reef fish.
   - ☐ c. the slowest of sea swimmers.
   - ☐ d. an example of colorful fish.

6. Something which is fluorescent
   - ☐ a. glows with its own light.
   - ☐ b. is distinct.
   - ☐ c. is flower-like.
   - ☐ d. reflects bright light.

CATEGORIES OF COMPREHENSION QUESTIONS

No. 1: Subject Matter	No. 3: Supporting Details	No. 5: Clarifying Devices
No. 2: Main Idea	No. 4: Conclusion	No. 6: Vocabulary in Context

37. EARLY MEASURES

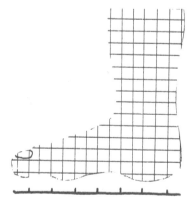

When life was rugged and simple, man's needs were few and he could supply them all. As he advanced from lone hunter to farmer and builder and exchanged a solitary existence for the greater comfort and security of community life, he realized he must come to an agreement with his neighbors on a common system of measurement. How can men build a house, or a storage hut, or a temple, unless all the builders use the same basic measurements?

The very earliest measurements were for length. The bases for the measures were those most natural—a foot, a palm, a span of the hand. When building alone, man could use his own body. But on community projects a common standard was required. The leader's measurements were taken and marked off on a stick or stone. Crude copies were made from the original and passed out for use. Later the foot gradually evolved to become twelve inches long.

1. This article could best be titled:
   ☐ a. Building a Hut.
   ☐ b. Man's Early Problems.
   ☐ c. Development of a Standardized Measurement.
   ☐ d. The Growth of Communities.

2. The advance of man from solitary to communal life created
   ☐ a. a decrease in his needs.
   ☐ b. the dominance of tribal leaders.
   ☐ c. a great demand for storage huts.
   ☐ d. a need for standards of measure.

3. The earliest measurements for length were
   ☐ a. determined by a stick.
   ☐ b. derived from parts of the body.
   ☐ c. used to build temples.
   ☐ d. the same as those used today.

4. Some standardization of measurement occurred
   ☐ a. as a result of a dispute over the proper size for a hut.
   ☐ b. because everyone's foot used to be almost the same length.
   ☐ c. due to the accidental discovery that a foot equalled twelve inches.
   ☐ d. when the leader's measurements replaced the individuals.

5. The author develops his point by means of
   ☐ a. factual explanation.
   ☐ b. comparison and contrast.
   ☐ c. arguments and proof.
   ☐ d. persuasion.

6. A person who has a solitary existence lives
   ☐ a. quietly.
   ☐ b. alone.
   ☐ c. with others.
   ☐ d. in jail.

CATEGORIES OF COMPREHENSION QUESTIONS

No. 1: Subject Matter	No. 3: Supporting Details	No. 5: Clarifying Devices
No. 2: Main Idea	No. 4: Conclusion	No. 6: Vocabulary in Context

38. THE PLEASING PENGUIN

There is distinguished evidence that penguins enjoy some types of music. The polar explorer Robert F. Scott noted that penguins would always "come up at a trot" when his men were singing, and he says that several of his men could frequently be found on the deck of the ship singing before an "admiring group of penguins." Sir Ernest Henry Shackelton observed the same thing. But apparently penguins are somewhat priggish about their music. A phonograph was put out on the ice, and soon a crowd of penguins gathered around, and apparently listened with pleasure and interest. This continued for a time, but when the music, which had been sedate, became frivolous, the birds began to be uneasy. Then the record was changed to "Waltz Me Around Again, Willie." This was too much for the penguins. For a moment, a moment only, the birds waited; then, with one mind they turned, squawking disgustedly, and went off. Their ancient dignity had been profaned.

1. The best title for this article is:
   - ☐ a. Robert F. Scott's Phonograph.
   - ☐ b. Lullabies in Birdland.
   - ☐ c. Discriminating Penguins.
   - ☐ d. Cool Tunes.

2. Penguins seem
   - ☐ a. to cluster always in groups.
   - ☐ b. to be able to dance to music.
   - ☐ c. to communicate with musical cries.
   - ☐ d. to appreciate music.

3. Scott's men were able
   - ☐ a. to imitate penguin mating cries.
   - ☐ b. to train penguins with music.
   - ☐ c. to record penguin songs.
   - ☐ d. to attract penguins with their singing.

4. Penguins apparently prefer
   - ☐ a. frivolous music.
   - ☐ b. calm, peaceful music.
   - ☐ c. any music compared to no music.
   - ☐ d. live singing to recorded music.

5. To develop his point, the author uses
   - ☐ a. factual description.
   - ☐ b. arguments and proof.
   - ☐ c. personal opinion.
   - ☐ d. persuasion.

6. The word priggish, as used in this article, most nearly means
   - ☐ a. pig-like.
   - ☐ b. careless.
   - ☐ c. particular.
   - ☐ d. ignorant.

CATEGORIES OF COMPREHENSION QUESTIONS

No. 1: Subject Matter	No. 3: Supporting Details	No. 5: Clarifying Devices
No. 2: Main Idea	No. 4: Conclusion	No. 6: Vocabulary in Context

39. SAY IT WITHOUT WORDS

Milady of a few centuries ago had a deuce of a time getting the word to a prospective suitor past a hovering chaperone unless she— and he—knew the flirt-fan routine. The array of signals grew into a most involved series of intricate gestures. By seemingly small, innocent movements of her fan, milady could relay to the gentleman when and where she could meet him, who might be with her, or whether or not she was in love with him.

This type of sign language had a reincarnation only a few years ago with the bobbysoxers. The thick short socks worn straight up meant the wearer was open for a date. One fold signified she was going steady, and rolled down meant taken, so stay away. Beads also have been used to indicate similar translations. Knotted at the neck the beads had the same meaning as rolled-down bobbysocks—"dated." But unknotted and hanging free, the beads said the wearer was available.

1. This selection deals with
   - ☐ a. communicating by symbols.
   - ☐ b. how to fool the chaperone.
   - ☐ c. old-style love affairs.
   - ☐ d. changing styles in flirting.

2. In this example, signals are used
   - ☐ a. to carry on complex conversations.
   - ☐ b. to indicate a woman's availability.
   - ☐ c. to show that one is stylish.
   - ☐ d. to express disapproval of a person's clothes.

3. Bobbysocks worn straight up indicated
   - ☐ a. a girl with attractive ankles.
   - ☐ b. that the wearer dressed neatly.
   - ☐ c. that the girl was available for dating.
   - ☐ d. that the wearer's legs were cold.

4. Through the use of sign language, one can
   - ☐ a. communicate without words.
   - ☐ b. fool a chaperone.
   - ☐ c. make dangerous mistakes.
   - ☐ d. communicate over great distances.

5. The author concerns himself with socks and beads because
   - ☐ a. he is aware of women's fashions.
   - ☐ b. they can be used as non-verbal cues.
   - ☐ c. they are more popular today than fans.
   - ☐ d. they can be dangerous if misunderstood.

6. A reincarnation is
   - ☐ a. a flower worn by bobbysoxers.
   - ☐ b. an ornate fan.
   - ☐ c. a type of sign language.
   - ☐ d. a new life.

CATEGORIES OF COMPREHENSION QUESTIONS

| No. 1: Subject Matter | No. 3: Supporting Details | No. 5: Clarifying Devices |
| No. 2: Main Idea | No. 4: Conclusion | No. 6: Vocabulary in Context |

40. LONG MAY IT LEAN!

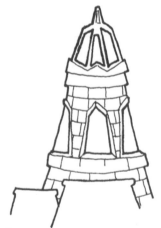

The Spanish city of Zaragoza once possessed a bell tower of exceedingly beautiful design dating back to the 16th century. The Torre Nueva was known throughout the world for its architectural perfection. Soaring almost 300 feet into the air, and faced with delicate stone tracery, it stood in a populated part of the city, surrounded by small shops and homes. But it began to decline slowly following its completion. By 1847, the tower had reached a menacing nine-foot lean and people who lived and worked under its looming threat petitioned the city to have it taken down. But so proud were the Zaragozans of the Torre Nueva and its link with the city's long history, that opposition quickly arose. The controversy dragged on for almost 50 years.

In 1893 the decision was reluctantly made that, for safety's sake, the ancient shaft would have to be demolished. Stone by stone, the Torre Nueva disappeared, until no physical trace of it remained. Today, it exists only in the memories of the people, who still regret that some way could not have been found to preserve it.

1. The best title for this selection would be:
   - ☐ a. The Leaning Tower of Pisa.
   - ☐ b. The Demise of the Torre Nueva.
   - ☐ c. Architecture of Northern Spain.
   - ☐ d. The Threat of Leaning Towers.

2. The people of Zaragoza opposed the plan to destroy the tower primarily because of its
   - ☐ a. beauty.
   - ☐ b. utility.
   - ☐ c. size.
   - ☐ d. location.

3. The tower was demolished in the year
   - ☐ a. 1528.
   - ☐ b. 1647.
   - ☐ c. 1847.
   - ☐ d. 1893.

4. The leaning tower was a threat because of its
   - ☐ a. age.
   - ☐ b. location.
   - ☐ c. utility.
   - ☐ d. history.

5. When the author says that the tower "exists" today he means it
   - ☐ a. still remains.
   - ☐ b. was reassembled.
   - ☐ c. is remembered.
   - ☐ d. fell suddenly.

6. The best synonym for tracery as it is used in this selection would be
   - ☐ a. ornaments.
   - ☐ b. pillars.
   - ☐ c. bricks.
   - ☐ d. windows.

CATEGORIES OF COMPREHENSION QUESTIONS

No. 1: Subject Matter	No. 3: Supporting Details	No. 5: Clarifying Devices
No. 2: Main Idea	No. 4: Conclusion	No. 6: Vocabulary in Context

41. PALMYRA: ANCIENT CITY

 Palmyra, an ancient city in Syria, was once nothing but a mud-hut oasis called Tadmore, a tiny village at the junction of two great trading routes. Then King Solomon erected a temple there to direct the wealth of the far-off east toward his kingdom. But Tadmore remained an obscure desert outpost until just prior to the birth of Jesus. Then, suddenly, with a shift in world powers, Palmyra began to grow.

Almost midway in the desert, 150 miles from Damascus and 190 miles—four day's journey by swift camel—from the Euphrates, it lay on the shortest route between the Phoenician coastal towns that gathered the rich merchandise of the western world and the Mesopotamian cities that commanded the fabulous eastern trade. To the west stood the mighty empire of Rome; to the east, the savage Parthians. Neither felt confident enough to wage war against the other. Swiftly, almost like a boom town privileged by both sides, Palmyra waxed rich and important as a trading center, a balance wheel and bulwark between two hesitant enemies.

1. The best title for this passage would be:
   ☐ a. Strategic Location.
   ☐ b. Shift in World Powers.
   ☐ c. Romans Against Parthians.
   ☐ d. From Oasis to Trade Center.

2. Palmyra's growth was a result of
   ☐ a. the construction of King Solomon's temple.
   ☐ b. its importance as an oasis.
   ☐ c. the generosity of the Romans and Parthians.
   ☐ d. a power shift and its good location.

3. A trip from Palmyra to Damascus would take about
   ☐ a. two days.
   ☐ b. four days.
   ☐ c. three days.
   ☐ d. six days.

4. This passage implies that Palmyra's military power was
   ☐ a. greater than Rome's.
   ☐ b. less than Rome's.
   ☐ c. equal to Rome's.
   ☐ d. declining rapidly.

5. The mileage distances mentioned in the second paragraph illustrate Palmyra's
   ☐ a. poor location.
   ☐ b. mid-position.
   ☐ c. isolation.
   ☐ d. great size.

6. The best synonym for <u>waxed</u> as used in this passage is
   ☐ a. changed.
   ☐ b. remained.
   ☐ c. grew.
   ☐ d. appeared.

CATEGORIES OF COMPREHENSION QUESTIONS

No. 1: Subject Matter	No. 3: Supporting Details	No. 5: Clarifying Devices
No. 2: Main Idea	No. 4: Conclusion	No. 6: Vocabulary in Context

42. OASIS FRUIT

 Probably the oldest known cultivated tree, the date palm has always seen yeoman service especially in the Arab Middle East where it is believed to have originated. Its fruit, the date, is a staple food. Dates can be eaten raw, cooked, baked into cakes or pressed into a delicious syrup that Arabs relish. Rich in carbohydrates, dates contain little fat and about 40 calories an ounce. The longevity of many Bedouins of the desert lands has been attributed, at least in part, to the nutritional benefits of the date, which ranks so importantly in their diet.

Its use as a food source accounts for only one asset of the date palm. The trunk makes excellent house-building timber; the midribs of the larger leaves go into furniture and into crates—for shipping dates! The leaflets of the tree are woven into baskets and floor mats; the fibrous portions of the trunk supply rope; the larger fronds are braided into fences, erected to break the advance of sand dunes. Even the stones of the date do not go unused. Crushed, they are fed to livestock as fodder.

1. This article could best be titled:
   ☐ a. The Nutritional Value of Dates.
   ☐ b. Date Palms—Trees of Many Uses.
   ☐ c. Basket Weaving in Arabia.
   ☐ d. Stopping the Sand Dunes.

2. Date palms
   ☐ a. are delicious raw or cooked.
   ☐ b. are worshiped in yeoman services.
   ☐ c. supply food and materials.
   ☐ d. are often braided into fences.

3. Dates
   ☐ a. are nutritionally rich.
   ☐ b. cause Bedouins to die young.
   ☐ c. are shipped in sacks.
   ☐ d. are used in building houses.

4. Nothing
   ☐ a. is more important to Arabs than dates.
   ☐ b. other than dates is eaten by Bedouins.
   ☐ c. is prettier than a palm oasis.
   ☐ d. goes to waste on a date palm.

5. The author uses
   ☐ a. analogy.
   ☐ b. contrast.
   ☐ c. description.
   ☐ d. comparison.

6. The word <u>asset</u> means
   ☐ a. type.
   ☐ b. aspect.
   ☐ c. small donkey.
   ☐ d. value.

CATEGORIES OF COMPREHENSION QUESTIONS

No. 1: Subject Matter	No. 3: Supporting Details	No. 5: Clarifying Devices
No. 2: Main Idea	No. 4: Conclusion	No. 6: Vocabulary in Context

43. FABRIC FROM THE PAST

There's no doubt that primitive mankind first trod the world without the benefit of clothing. Historians suggest that thousands, perhaps millions of years passed before animal skins became fashionable. Then, sometime in the dim past, man discovered that the hair of certain animals pressed together stayed together. The fabric known as felt replaced animal skins. No one knows the age of felt—only that it was in use long before Neolithic man learned how to weave cloth a mere twelve thousand years ago.

The manufacture of felt is simple. Seen through a microscope, the hair of many animals appears as a barbed strand, the barbs all pointing toward the tip of the hair. When a number of hairs are pressed together, those which lie in opposite directions <u>interlock</u> barbs and resist efforts to pull them apart.

Legend has it that St. Clement (patron saint of felt makers) discovered felt when, at the beginning of a long journey, he put carded wool between his feet and the soles of his sandals. When he reached his destination, he found no carded wool in his sandals. The wool had been compressed into felt.

1. This passage is about
   □ a. felt, the saviour of mankind.
   □ b. the first man-made fabric.
   □ c. St. Clement, inventor of the sandal.
   □ d. the manufacture of artificial hides.

2. Before the invention of felt, man was forced
   □ a. to wear clothes of woven fabric.
   □ b. to swing naked through the trees.
   □ c. to wear sandals made of carded wool.
   □ d. to wear the skins of animals.

3. The manufacture of felt utilizes
   □ a. a chemical reaction between wool and leather.
   □ b. pressure applied over a period of time.
   □ c. the peculiar physical characteristics of some animal hairs.
   □ d. the wool carder and the microscope.

4. The author portrays felt as
   □ a. the gift of St. Clement to man.
   □ b. the bridge between animal hides and woven cloth.
   □ c. a strong, lightweight, durable fabric.
   □ d. a material used for padding sandals.

5. The author gives
   □ a. the age, manufacturing process and origin of felt.
   □ b. reasons why felt was not discovered earlier.
   □ c. a comparison of the merits of felt and wool.
   □ d. conflicting viewpoints of the importance of felt.

6. To <u>interlock</u> is
   □ a. to interpret or explain.
   □ b. to lock inside or imprison.
   □ c. to unite or interlace firmly.
   □ d. to compress with great pressure.

CATEGORIES OF COMPREHENSION QUESTIONS

| No. 1: Subject Matter | No. 3: Supporting Details | No. 5: Clarifying Devices |
| No. 2: Main Idea | No. 4: Conclusion | No. 6: Vocabulary in Context |

44. MUSIC IN THE STREETS

Today's street organs are huge, complicated instruments that require experts to operate and maintain, but they were not always so big. The first barrel or hand organs that came to Amsterdam about 1850 were small enough to be carried around by one man, strapped to his back. They contained a cylinder dotted with pins and points that created music when cranked by striking built-in flutes, much like a music box. Most of these early street organs came from a firm in Paris and one in Germany's Black Forest. Later organ builders constructed large cylinder instruments designed for dance halls and fairs, but no one thought of building out-sized organs for use in city streets.

No one, that is, until Leon Warnies, a blind Belgian, settled down in Amsterdam. His idea, in 1875, was to lease cylinder organs to street musicians, and his Rent-an-Organ business soon proved that everyone—kids and adults—could dig up a spare coin to hear a bit of an opera, a thundering military march, or a hit tune of the day. Those coins enabled Warnies to order larger organs, so large and heavy, in fact, that three-wheeled carriages had to be placed under them. The single operator gave way to a three-man crew that <u>maneuvered</u> the weighty organ through narrow streets. It's still done the same way today. The boss of the crew, the one who holds the street musician's license, hires the organ. The second man, the organ grinder, is usually a strong fellow for he must apply muscle to the big wheel that cranks out the music. The third man helps the boss collect the money, and all three lend a hand when it's time to push the organ to another street or square.

1. This passage is concerned with the
   □ a. history of organs.
   □ b. development of the street organ.
   □ c. music in the Amsterdam towns.
   □ d. entertainment of the 1800s.

2. Something which was not a forerunner of the three-man street organ is the
   □ a. dance hall organ.
   □ b. barrel organ.
   □ c. music box.
   □ d. cylinder organ.

3. Leon Warnies' innovation brought
   □ a. booming business to Amsterdam.
   □ b. music into the streets.
   □ c. organs into dance halls and fairs.
   □ d. an increase in the number of street musicians.

4. The author implies that street organs were
   □ a. a nuisance.
   □ b. an economic boost.
   □ c. historically linked to music boxes.
   □ d. an innovation in entertainment.

5. The author develops his point by means of
   □ a. narration and description.
   □ b. precise details.
   □ c. contrast.
   □ d. intricate comparisons.

6. The word maneuvered, as used in the passage, means
   □ a. pulled with difficulty.
   □ b. pushed with great care.
   □ c. operated with skill.
   □ d. maintained in good condition.

CATEGORIES OF COMPREHENSION QUESTIONS

No. 1: Subject Matter	No. 3: Supporting Details	No. 5: Clarifying Devices
No. 2: Main Idea	No. 4: Conclusion	No. 6: Vocabulary in Context

45. SIGNS OF SPRING

Canada geese arrive when the average daily temperature reaches 35 degrees. The "honkers" apparently consider this the front line of spring, for it melts the ice on the lakes they love. When the temperature hits a steady 35 degrees in Washington, D.C., the geese can be found on nearby Chesapeake Bay. By March 30, when the water at Portsmouth, New Hampshire has cleared, the geese are winging across Quebec, headed for Hudson Bay, where it is never spring without them.

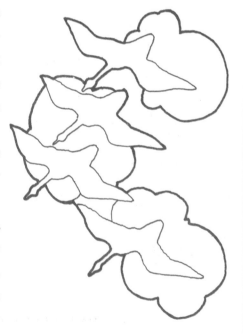

1. The best title for this selection would be:
   - ☐ a. Homing Instincts of Birds.
   - ☐ b. The Migration of Geese.
   - ☐ c. The Movement of Spring.
   - ☐ d. The Rites of Spring.

2. Spring begins on the same day in all parts of the hemisphere. The front that moves is
   - ☐ a. average humidity.
   - ☐ b. average daily temperature.
   - ☐ c. average position of geese.
   - ☐ d. average rainfall per month.

3. At what average daily temperature are geese found?
   - ☐ a. 30 degrees
   - ☐ b. 35 degrees
   - ☐ c. 40 degrees
   - ☐ d. 45 degrees

4. This paragraph suggests that the point at which spring weather begins in the Northern Hemisphere
   - ☐ a. moves northward with time.
   - ☐ b. moves southward in March.
   - ☐ c. is the same at all times.
   - ☐ d. progresses eastward during spring.

5. The author calls the birds "honkers" in order
   - ☐ a. to describe their calls.
   - ☐ b. to avoid repetition of "geese."
   - ☐ c. to clarify his point.
   - ☐ d. to emphasize their importance.

6. The best synonym for winging as it is used in this selection is
   - ☐ a. traveling.
   - ☐ b. flying.
   - ☐ c. escaping.
   - ☐ d. migrating.

CATEGORIES OF COMPREHENSION QUESTIONS

| No. 1: Subject Matter | No. 3: Supporting Details | No. 5: Clarifying Devices |
| No. 2: Main Idea | No. 4: Conclusion | No. 6: Vocabulary in Context |

46. THE HOLLYWOOD FLY MAN

Motion pictures and television have created <u>subtle</u> make-up problems that seem more closely related to the physics and chemistry of light, lenses, and film emulsions than to the cosmetic art. As the art has developed, experts have appeared, but none quite so odd as the Hollywood "fly man." Because grease paint is vitamin-rich and contains sugar, movie studio flies are attracted. So, while actors and actresses await their camera call, the "fly man" brushes the insects from their faces, which the performers themselves dare not touch.

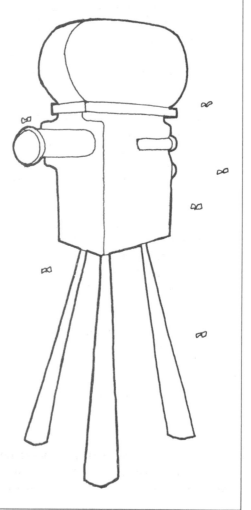

1. The subject matter of this passage is
   □ a. techniques for applying stage make-up.
   □ b. problems of acting.
   □ c. a problem connected with make-up.
   □ d. the appearance of Hollywood experts.

2. Hollywood make-up problems stem
   □ a. more from technical difficulties than the cosmetic art.
   □ b. from the use of grease paint.
   □ c. from the fact that the performers cannot touch their make-up.
   □ d. from the amount of time the performers must wait for their camera call.

3. The "fly man" discussed in the passage is
   □ a. a stunt man who does flying acts.
   □ b. a specialist in applying make-up.
   □ c. someone who brushes insects from actors' faces.
   □ d. the man who invented vitamin-rich grease paint.

4. We can conclude from the passage that the problem of using grease paint
   □ a. is outweighed by the advantages.
   □ b. is solved through the efforts of the "fly man."
   □ c. no longer exists.
   □ d. is typical when compared with other make-up problems.

5. The author develops his main idea in this passage through the use of
   □ a. proofs of points raised.
   □ b. vivid descriptions.
   □ c. a strong conclusion.
   □ d. problems and solutions.

6. The best meaning for <u>subtle</u> as used in the passage is
   □ a. of a variety of types.
   □ b. involving great expense.
   □ c. frequently occurring.
   □ d. difficult to understand.

CATEGORIES OF COMPREHENSION QUESTIONS

No. 1: Subject Matter	No. 3: Supporting Details	No. 5: Clarifying Devices
No. 2: Main Idea	No. 4: Conclusion	No. 6: Vocabulary in Context

47. WRITING FROM A TO Z

Among the great inventions of mankind, the alphabet stands alone. Unlike the axe, the lever, the wheel, the screw and the arch, which sprang into being relatively whole and full-blown, the alphabet is the product of thousands of years of painstaking development by thousands of men. Moreover, the evolution of the alphabet is destined to continue as long as man uses it. The alphabet stands apart in another, more important way. It was the fruit of a conscious and deliberate attempt by man to lend a touch of immortality to his transient life. To the extent that he succeeded, man alone of the animal kingdom has a history, and because of history, civilization.

1. The author's general topic in this passage is
   - ☐ a. the unimportance of the axe, the lever, the wheel, the screw and the arch.
   - ☐ b. the importance of the alphabet to mankind.
   - ☐ c. the difficulties of creating a usable alphabet.
   - ☐ d. the great age of the alphabet.

2. The main idea of this passage is that
   - ☐ a. painstaking efforts to evolve the alphabet continue to develop our civilization.
   - ☐ b. "a conscious and deliberate attempt" leads to success.
   - ☐ c. all civilized men need an alphabet.
   - ☐ d. the axe, lever, wheels, etc., are inventions along with the alphabet.

3. The "deliberate attempt" mentioned in the passage refers to man's effort to
   - ☐ a. communicate through written language.
   - ☐ b. use his mind.
   - ☐ c. create a civilization.
   - ☐ d. record his activities.

4. We can conclude from this passage that
   - ☐ a. the alphabet did not come into being overnight.
   - ☐ b. without an alphabet men could not communicate.
   - ☐ c. the alphabet is now perfected.
   - ☐ d. men will someday be able to get along without an alphabet.

5. In this passage, the author makes the point that
   - ☐ a. men created the alphabet in a search for immortality.
   - ☐ b. the use of the alphabet allows man to differ from other animals.
   - ☐ c. mechanical inventions are not important.
   - ☐ d. the creation of an alphabet was accidental.

6. As used in this passage, <u>transient</u> seems to mean
   - ☐ a. useless.
   - ☐ b. easy to see.
   - ☐ c. short, temporary.
   - ☐ d. moving from place to place.

CATEGORIES OF COMPREHENSION QUESTIONS

No. 1: Subject Matter	No. 3: Supporting Details	No. 5: Clarifying Devices
No. 2: Main Idea	No. 4: Conclusion	No. 6: Vocabulary in Context

48. BEARDS COME AND GO

On occasion public opinion and religion have cast a heavy shadow on the destiny of beards. New Englander Joseph Palmer was stoned and jailed in 1830 for daring to wear a beard in Fitchburg, Massachusetts. He persevered long enough to enjoy the satisfaction of seeing beards come strongly back during the Civil War and, as a stinging reminder to his neighbors, he saw to it that the epitaph on his tombstone read: "Persecuted for wearing the Beard." In 1907, public pressure caused the hotels of Paris to order their waiters to shave clean, thereby setting off a long strike. Not very long ago our own American public looked askance at an unbearded medical man.

1. This passage centers on the attitudes towards wearing beards
   - ☐ a. in Fitchburg, Massachusetts.
   - ☐ b. in the past.
   - ☐ c. by religious groups.
   - ☐ d. of employers.

2. In the past bearded men were chastised through
   - ☐ a. public opinion and religious pressure.
   - ☐ b. a stiff fine levied by the government.
   - ☐ c. an outrage campaign conducted by newspapers.
   - ☐ d. petitions by women's organizations.

3. For wearing a beard in 1830, Joseph Palmer was
   - ☐ a. praised.
   - ☐ b. ignored.
   - ☐ c. stoned.
   - ☐ d. laughed at.

4. We can conclude from this passage that, on occasion, bearded men have been
   - ☐ a. actually punished by public authorities.
   - ☐ b. excommunicated by church members.
   - ☐ c. highly approved of by their neighbors.
   - ☐ d. ridiculed in books, magazines, and newspapers.

5. The author develops his point through
   - ☐ a. straightforward anecdotal narrative.
   - ☐ b. dreamy imagery.
   - ☐ c. technical examples.
   - ☐ d. cause and effect.

6. Persecuted means
   - ☐ a. made to pay a fine.
   - ☐ b. classed as a criminal.
   - ☐ c. treated harshly.
   - ☐ d. remembered after death.

CATEGORIES OF COMPREHENSION QUESTIONS

No. 1: Subject Matter	No. 3: Supporting Details	No. 5: Clarifying Devices
No. 2: Main Idea	No. 4: Conclusion	No. 6: Vocabulary in Context

49. THE DEAD SEA

The Dead Sea is truly "dead." With water six times saltier than ocean water and with enormous quantities of other minerals stirred in besides, the Dead Sea can support life only in bacterial form. The Dead Sea is the lowest point on earth—1,300 feet below sea level; it is one of the hottest places on earth; and few if any birds inhabit the region. But the high salinity is neither lethal nor threatening. The searing, unbearable heat occurs only in the middle of the summer and birds avoid the sea not because it gives off any kind of <u>toxic</u> fumes, but because there are no fish or insects to eat.

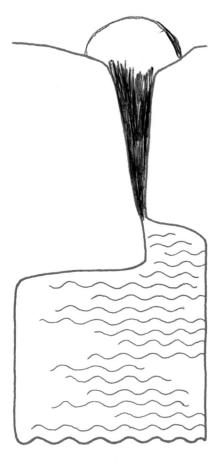

1. This passage is mainly concerned with the
   - ☐ a. hidden beauty of the Dead Sea.
   - ☐ b. fabled birds of the Dead Sea.
   - ☐ c. appropriately-named Dead Sea.
   - ☐ d. lovely Dead Sea resorts.

2. The Dead Sea
   - ☐ a. is an important bird sanctuary.
   - ☐ b. abounds with varied life forms.
   - ☐ c. is pleasant all year-round.
   - ☐ d. is dead but not deadly.

3. High salinity
   - ☐ a. causes Dead Sea fish to taste salty.
   - ☐ b. can be fatal to birds and humans.
   - ☐ c. can support only bacterial life.
   - ☐ d. occurs only in the summer months.

4. The Dead Sea
   - ☐ a. cannot support animal life.
   - ☐ b. permeates the atmosphere with poison.
   - ☐ c. caused sailors to be called "old salts."
   - ☐ d. is always unbearably hot.

5. The author uses
   - ☐ a. contrast and comparison.
   - ☐ b. descriptive narration.
   - ☐ c. conversation and dialogue.
   - ☐ d. figurative language.

6. The word <u>toxic</u> means
   - ☐ a. foul-smelling.
   - ☐ b. poisonous.
   - ☐ c. disgusting.
   - ☐ d. evil.

CATEGORIES OF COMPREHENSION QUESTIONS

No. 1: Subject Matter	No. 3: Supporting Details	No. 5: Clarifying Devices
No. 2: Main Idea	No. 4: Conclusion	No. 6: Vocabulary in Context

50. A FLOATING MESSAGE

Traditionally, messages inside floating bottles carry the SOS of shipwrecked sailors. These tragic and usually hopeless calls for help have, on occasion, <u>uncannily</u> made their way to a sailor's home port. One of the most dramatic coincidences on record concerns a Japanese seaman called Matsuyama. In 1784 he and forty-four companions set sail in search of treasure but met disaster instead. Dying of starvation on a coral reef in the Pacific, he carved his story on a piece of bark and sealed it in a bottle which he tossed into the ocean. In 1935, a century and a half later, this sturdy bottle bobbed upon the shore of Hiratutemura, the very place where Matsuyama was born!

1. The most appropriate title for the passage is:
   ☒ a. The Tale of Matsuyama.
   ☐ b. Floating Bottles.
   ☐ c. Tidings from the Sea.
   ☐ d. SOS: An Appeal for Help.

2. According to the passage,
   ☒ a. messages inside floating bottles sometimes reach other men.
   ☐ b. Matsuyama wanted to send his bottle home.
   ☐ c. Japanese are not good seamen.
   ☐ d. floating bottles are the best means for shipwrecked sailors to summon aid.

3. It is true that
   ☐ a. Matsuyama sent the first bottle message.
   ☐ b. it takes an average of a century and a half for messages to be found.
   ☒ c. sailors should not depend solely on floating bottles to request aid.
   ☐ d. the bottle was made of a high quality glass from Japan.

4. We can infer from reading the passage that
   ☒ a. Matsuyama was aware that his death was near.
   ☐ b. the seamen must have been extremely far from home.
   ☐ c. Japanese like to use floating bottles.
   ☐ d. floating bottles aren't too unreliable.

5. In writing the passage the author uses
   ☒ a. an illustrative story.
   ☐ b. arguments and proof.
   ☐ c. comparison and contrast.
   ☐ d. scientific facts.

6. As used in this passage, <u>uncannily</u> seems to mean
   ☐ a. uncleverly.
   ☐ b. fortunately.
   ☒ c. mysteriously.
   ☐ d. by the will of God.

CATEGORIES OF COMPREHENSION QUESTIONS		
No. 1: Subject Matter	No. 3: Supporting Details	No. 5: Clarifying Devices
No. 2: Main Idea	No. 4: Conclusion	No. 6: Vocabulary in Context

51. THE SHIFTING SANDS

An airplane flight over eastern Saudi Arabia will bring home with tremendous impact the magnitude of the sand migration problem. From the cabin window a passenger can view one sprawling dune, sixteen miles long and four miles wide, looming like a frozen tidal wave. It stands poised at the doorways of a dozen villages. Sand has already spilled into irrigation ditches and cut off drainage, and has clogged artesian wells and strangled crops. The dune has shouldered its bulk against the threshold of one of the kingdom's most precious assets—an oasis. Creeping at a slow, silent, but nonetheless merciless pace, the tons of sand promise to engulf the oasis unless its onward drive can be checked.

1. This passage could best be titled:
    - ■ a. Silent but Deadly.
    - ☐ b. Dune Buggy.
    - ☐ c. Sand—Arabia's Greatest Resource.
    - ☐ d. Beach Without Water.

2. The dune
    - ☐ a. can be seen only from an airplane.
    - ☐ b. can be kept out of villages by shutting doors.
    - ■ c. has done considerable damage and promises more.
    - ☐ d. is intensely destructive, but passes quickly.

3. The sand threatens to
    - ☐ a. clog artesian wells.
    - ☐ b. cause airplane crashes.
    - ■ c. bury an oasis.
    - ☐ d. overtake desert tortoises.

4. The dune
    - ☐ a. is more frightening than dangerous.
    - ☐ b. must be stopped at all costs.
    - ☐ c. fulfills man's need for a portable mountain.
    - ■ d. is the kingdom's most precious asset.

5. The author shows the nature of the creeping dune
    - ☐ a. by comparing it with a stationary dune.
    - ☐ b. through the use of simile and metaphor.
    - ☐ c. by glorifying its unmatched beauty.
    - ■ d. by listing its actual and potential effects.

6. As used in this passage, <u>migration</u> seems to mean
    - ☐ a. going from one country to another.
    - ■ b. movement.
    - ☐ c. seasonal change of residence.
    - ☐ d. temporary location.

CATEGORIES OF COMPREHENSION QUESTIONS

No. 1: Subject Matter	No. 3: Supporting Details	No. 5: Clarifying Devices
No. 2: Main Idea	No. 4: Conclusion	No. 6: Vocabulary in Context

52. THE BATTLE CALLED BUNKER HILL

On the night of June 16, General Artemas Ward sent about a thousand Yankees to Charlestown, to fortify Bunker Hill. Arriving officers looked at the two adjacent hills, Breed's and Bunker's (where Mr. Breed and Mr. Bunker pastured cows), and decided on Breed's. Every man took pickaxe or shovel and set to work in the darkness. At dawn, an American <u>redoubt</u> crowned Breed's Hill.

The astonished British prepared to accept this challenge. They could not guess how many Americans were behind the redoubt. They did not suspect that the Breed's Hill detachment was isolated, without food, water or sufficient ammunition, and with no plans for relief in case of attack.

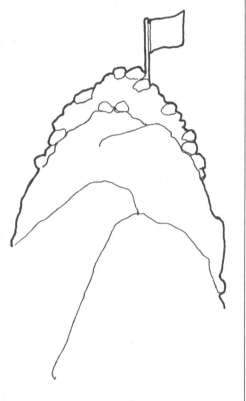

55

1. The best title for this selection would be:
   ☐ a. The Defense of Charlestown.
   ☐ b. Battle of Bunker Hill.
   ☑ c. Challenge at Breed's Hill.
   ☐ d. The Attack of Breed's Hill.

2. The British commanders were not aware that
   ☐ a. Breed's Hill was fortified.
   ☐ b. Yankee reinforcements were nearby.
   ☑ c. the Breed's Hill detachment was isolated.
   ☐ d. the Redcoats were outnumbered.

3. Breed's Hill and Bunker's Hill are
   ☐ a. two names for the same hill.
   ☑ b. next to each other.
   ☐ c. twenty miles apart.
   ☐ d. twenty miles from Charlestown.

4. The strategy that the Americans used in the defense of Breed's Hill against the British was
   ☐ a. to plan an ambush at Bunker Hill.
   ☑ b. to create the illusion that they had a larger army.
   ☐ c. to overwhelm them by sheer numbers.
   ☐ d. to form a lasting peace agreement.

5. The concluding sentence of this passage is used to show that the American soldiers were
   ☐ a. careless.
   ☐ b. inferior.
   ☑ c. courageous.
   ☐ d. well-organized.

6. As it is used in this selection, <u>redoubt</u> means
   ☐ a. hidden caves.
   ☐ b. a concealing hill of earth.
   ☑ c. elaborate trenches.
   ☐ d. a tunnel under the enemy's position.

CATEGORIES OF COMPREHENSION QUESTIONS		
No. 1: Subject Matter	No. 3: Supporting Details	No. 5: Clarifying Devices
No. 2: Main Idea	No. 4: Conclusion	No. 6: Vocabulary in Context

53. NATURE'S HARDIEST

Trees have developed special talents for surviving in the desert. Like the cactus they, too, have water reservoirs in their trunks or in their stems below the ground. The most stoical desert trees have sparse, leathery, or spiky foliage or may even dispense with leaves completely, as the cactus does. Many are protected by thorns. In the most inhospitable areas of the American Southwest, the spiny mesquite or screw bean survives— even in Death Valley. In the waterless places of Arabia the *nibq* struggles against adversity where the dates cannot grow "with their feet in water and their heads in the fires of heaven," and produces a fruit, the *dom,* so profusely that passers-by are allowed to shake the small berries from the branches.

1. This passage centers around
   ☐ a. cactus trees.
   ☐ b. special talents of trees.
   ☐ c. trees that can survive in the desert.
   ☐ d. the *dom.*

2. What is the main idea of this passage?
   ☐ a. Some trees have developed special talents to adapt to the desert.
   ☐ b. Most desert trees have spiky foliage.
   ☐ c. Several deserts have desert trees.
   ☐ d. Most trees are well-protected and can readily survive desert conditions.

3. The *nibq* is a desert tree
   ☐ a. which is similar to the date tree.
   ☐ b. found in some areas of Arabia.
   ☐ c. that scarcely produces a fruit, the *dom.*
   ☐ d. that has a hard time fighting the weather conditions.

4. We would not expect a tree in the desert
   ☐ a. to have branches.
   ☐ b. to live for a long time.
   ☐ c. to have water reservoirs.
   ☐ d. to have numerous leaves.

5. In developing this passage, the author uses
   ☐ a. cause and effect.
   ☐ b. contrasts.
   ☐ c. logical reasoning from facts.
   ☐ d. examples and comparison.

6. As used in this passage <u>stoical</u> means
   ☐ a. succulent.
   ☐ b. able to hold water.
   ☐ c. showing indifference to outside conditions.
   ☐ d. heavily built at base of trunk.

CATEGORIES OF COMPREHENSION QUESTIONS		
No. 1: Subject Matter	No. 3: Supporting Details	No. 5: Clarifying Devices
No. 2: Main Idea	No. 4: Conclusion	No. 6: Vocabulary in Context

54. THE SAUSAGE

Despite the enormous quantities of sausages they consume each year, few Americans are acquainted with the names of the numerous varieties available in this country. A recent survey showed that less than 50 percent know any names beyond frankfurter, Bologna and salami.

Buyers usually walk into a delicatessen or butcher shop and point mutely to the loaf or link that strikes their fancy.

If you were to compile the names of all the types of sausage available in the world, you'd wind up with nearly 500 names on your list. There are more than 100 kinds—domestic and imported—sold in the United States alone.

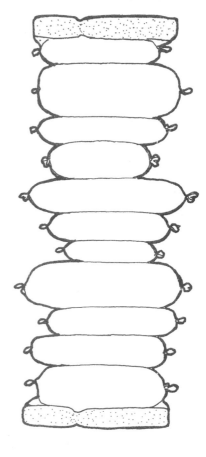

1. In the paragraph the author focuses on
   □ a. American sausages and European sausages.
   □ b. salami, frankfurters and Bologna.
   ☑ c. sausages available to Americans.
   □ d. foreign sausages sold in the United States.

2. The main idea that the author tries to get across is
   □ a. most Americans don't like the many foreign sausages.
   ☑ b. many Americans are unfamiliar with the variety of sausages.
   □ c. people are beginning to buy a lot of sausages at butchers.
   □ d. that it is best to be silent when you don't know the name of a sausage.

3. Less than fifty percent of the Americans surveyed
   □ a. can name every kind of sausage, domestic and imported.
   □ b. eat only salami, Bologna, and frankfurters.
   □ c. know what salami, Bologna, and frankfurters are.
   ☑ d. know any sausage names besides frankfurter, Bologna and salami.

4. After reading the passage, the best conclusion might be that
   □ a. most people are afraid to eat foreign sausages.
   □ b. domestic sausage is not sold outside the United States.
   □ c. people don't usually talk in butcher shops unless they know the names of sausages.
   ☑ d. frankfurters, Bologna and salami are the most popular types of sausage in the United States.

5. In developing the main point of the paragraph, the author uses all of the following except
   □ a. statistics.
   □ b. comparison.
   ☑ c. arguments.
   □ d. information.

6. The best meaning of <u>fancy</u> in the paragraph is
   □ a. imagination.
   □ b. elaboration.
   ☑ c. liking.
   □ d. very critical taste.

CATEGORIES OF COMPREHENSION QUESTIONS

No. 1: Subject Matter	No. 3: Supporting Details	No. 5: Clarifying Devices
No. 2: Main Idea	No. 4: Conclusion	No. 6: Vocabulary in Context

55. SIGNS OF SPRING

All those young men who find that in spring their fancies "lightly turn to thoughts of love," might regard the arrival of spring as mysterious. On the other hand, the scientifically-minded find nothing mysterious; they have been expecting it right along—expecting it, in fact, at precisely 3:32 P.M. on March 20. At that moment the sun balances itself on the celestial equator, an imaginary line passing through the heavens above the earth's belt. Its warmth is equally divided north and south, and in all parts of the world, night and day are of equal length. That instant in March is called the vernal equinox, and an instant later the sun swings into the northern skies. Its slanting rays bring spring to the Northern Hemisphere. Spring gains momentum during the closing days of March and by April it is busting out all over.

1. The best title for this selection would be:
   - ☐ a. Human Biological Rhythms.
   - ☐ b. Variation in the Vernal Equinox.
   - ☐ c. The Coming of Spring. ✗
   - ☑ d. The Mystery of Spring.

2. The underlying cause of spring is the
   - ☐ a. length of day increase.
   - ☐ b. angle of the sun to the earth. ✗
   - ☐ c. increase in average temperature.
   - ☑ d. change in celestial equator.

3. At the vernal equinox the length of the day is
   - ☑ a. greater than the length of night.
   - ☐ b. less than the length of night.
   - ☐ c. equal to the length of night. ✗
   - ☐ d. the longest of the year.

4. Spring in the Southern Hemisphere would occur during the season which we call
   - ☑ a. spring.
   - ☑ b. fall.
   - ☐ c. summer. ✓
   - ☐ d. winter.

5. The author describes the effect of spring on young men to show that the arrival of the season
   - ☑ a. seems mysterious. ✓
   - ☐ b. has little effect.
   - ☐ c. directly affects men.
   - ☐ d. is hard to detect.

6. The best synonym for <u>momentum</u> as it is used in this selection would be
   - ☐ a. time.
   - ☑ b. strength. ✓
   - ☐ c. speed.
   - ☐ d. impetus.

CATEGORIES OF COMPREHENSION QUESTIONS

No. 1: Subject Matter	No. 3: Supporting Details	No. 5: Clarifying Devices
No. 2: Main Idea	No. 4: Conclusion	No. 6: Vocabulary in Context

56. PEOPLE LIKE PICKLES

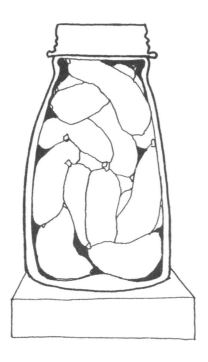

It was Thomas Jefferson who wrote:

"On a hot day in Virginia, I know of nothing more comforting than a firm, spiced pickle, brought up trout-like from the sparkling depths of that aromatic jar below stairs in Aunt Sally's cellar."

The common yen for pickles that has existed since the earliest records of man, although the result of his more capricious taste buds, is not entirely without benefit. Recent studies show pickles to contain vitamins A, B_1, B_2, and best of all, generous quantities of vitamin C, a substance most essential to good health.

It must have been instinct or good luck that guided explorers during the Middle Ages to stock heavily with pickles during those long voyages into the unknown, voyages often plagued with attacks of vitamin deficiencies such as beriberi and scurvy.

1. This article could also be titled:
   - ☐ a. The Peter Piper Story.
   - ☐ b. Why Pickles Are Good to Grow.
   - ■ c. Good News for Pickle Lovers.
   - ☐ d. The Pickle Metamorphosis.

2. Pickles are discussed primarily to show that they
   - ☐ a. were enjoyed by Thomas Jefferson.
   - ■ b. are healthful as well as tasty.
   - ☐ c. were used to fight scurvy.
   - ☐ d. have been around for many years.

3. One thing which is not said about pickles is that
   - ■ a. in excess, they cause scurvy.
   - ☐ b. they were enjoyed by Thomas Jefferson.
   - ☐ c. they contain four important vitamins.
   - ☐ d. they were eaten even during the Middle Ages.

4. Man's yen for pickles
   - ☐ a. was glorified by Thomas Jefferson.
   - ☐ b. has been greatly exaggerated.
   - ☐ c. is an aromatic habit.
   - ■ d. protected him from vitamin deficiencies.

5. To make his point the author uses
   - ■ a. the technique of contrast and comparison.
   - ☐ b. unsubstantiated opinion.
   - ☐ c. facts as the basis for his opinion.
   - ☐ d. simple chronological order of events.

6. As used in this passage, plagued with seems to mean
   - ☐ a. teased by.
   - ☐ b. canceled by.
   - ☐ c. made successful by.
   - ■ d. troubled by.

CATEGORIES OF COMPREHENSION QUESTIONS

No. 1: Subject Matter	No. 3: Supporting Details	No. 5: Clarifying Devices
No. 2: Main Idea	No. 4: Conclusion	No. 6: Vocabulary in Context

57. PASS THE PEPPER, PLEASE

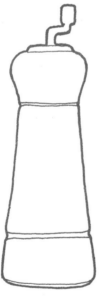

Pepper was, for many years, man's first means of refrigeration: during the Crusades pepper was used to preserve sausages. In 1956, some twenty percent of the pepper imported was sold to meat packers in this country.

Pepper-mills are now common household items, but restaurants which went along with the trend and put pepper-mills on their tables found they had to retrieve them after the entree—too many customers were "collecting" pepper-mills.

Pepper has also been considered as a medicine. One medieval book of cures recommends that to cure aches and pains "the patient is to take nine peppercorns." The Egyptians used pepper for embalming, and Indians use it today to cure toothaches. Pepper is used by French and Dutch housewives to kill moths and as an insect repellent.

1. The subject matter of this passage is
   - ☐ a. the use of the "black salt."
   - ☐ b. pepper as a form of refrigeration.
   - ☐ c. small inventions and improvements.
   - ■ d. pepper and its uses.

2. The author's main thought is that
   - ■ a. pepper has been used for a long time and for various reasons.
   - ☐ b. without pepper much meat would have been lost and many illnesses not cured.
   - ☐ c. pepper-mills are very common household items.
   - ☐ d. pepper is the most useful of all seasonings.

3. According to this passage, pepper has been used for all of the following except
   - ☐ a. to cure toothache.
   - ■ b. to exterminate ants.
   - ☐ c. to preserve dead bodies.
   - ☐ d. to relieve aches and pains.

4. We can conclude from the passage that pepper.
   - ☐ a. must be the most desirable spice of all.
   - ■ b. has been useful in many ways for centuries.
   - ☐ c. is not easily spoiled and is a beneficial medicine.
   - ☐ d. costs very little since its supply seems unlimited.

5. The author presents his ideas in this passage through
   - ☐ a. unsupported statements.
   - ☐ b. contrast and comparison.
   - ☐ c. arguments and proof.
   - ■ d. citing examples.

6. As the word is used in this passage, refrigeration means a way
   - ■ a. to keep meats from spoiling.
   - ☐ b. to keep things cold.
   - ☐ c. to make ice cubes.
   - ☐ d. to season meat products.

CATEGORIES OF COMPREHENSION QUESTIONS		
No. 1: Subject Matter	No. 3: Supporting Details	No. 5: Clarifying Devices
No. 2: Main Idea	No. 4: Conclusion	No. 6: Vocabulary in Context

58. THE TWO FACES OF APRIL

Above all else April has been known for her showers. The song Al Jolson made famous is simply a modern elaboration of the old weather saying familiar to generations: "April showers bring May flowers." Small wonder, then, if we assume April to be a very wet affair. Strangely enough, however, modern weather records show that—in the United States, at least—nowhere is April the wettest month! Summer showers, on the whole, are heavier than those of spring; and the frontal rains of winter storms are longer and steadier. What gives April a reputation for showery weather, it seems, is her chameleon-like change of humor. Meteorologists use phrases like "spring depressions," "meridional flow," and "mobile air masses" to explain the crazy quilt of mixed weather that marks the seasons' turning.

1. This selection would best be titled:
   - ☐ a. Spring and Storm.
   - ☐ b. Happiness Is in April.
   - ☑ c. The April Myth.
   - ☐ d. Soggy April.

2. The author's main purpose in discussing April is to show that it
   - ☐ a. is no longer the wet month it once was.
   - ☐ b. gives rise to the flowers of later spring.
   - ☐ c. is attractive to songwriters.
   - ☑ d. doesn't really live up to its rainy reputation.

3. On the whole, spring showers are
   - ☑ a. lighter than those of summer.
   - ☐ b. longer but less harmful than those of winter.
   - ☐ c. shorter but steadier than those of winter.
   - ☐ d. the loveliest kind of showers.

4. April's reputation as a wet month suggests that
   - ☐ a. songwriters are usually unreliable.
   - ☑ b. it is often a gloomy month.
   - ☐ c. meteorologists don't know all the answers about the weather.
   - ☐ d. reputations are not always based on fact.

5. The author makes his case by
   - ☐ a. the use of unproven information.
   - ☐ b. presenting a traditional idea and disputing it by using facts.
   - ☑ c. contrasting his ideas with those of meteorologists.
   - ☐ d. making unproven assumptions.

6. To say that April exhibits a chameleon-like change of humor means that April
   - ☐ a. causes certain people to have special feelings about it.
   - ☐ b. defies the knowledge of meteorologists.
   - ☑ c. is unpredictable and variable.
   - ☐ d. reflects the personalities of people.

CATEGORIES OF COMPREHENSION QUESTIONS

No. 1: Subject Matter	No. 3: Supporting Details	No. 5: Clarifying Devices
No. 2: Main Idea	No. 4: Conclusion	No. 6: Vocabulary in Context

59. JUNIYAH: JEWEL OF LEBANON

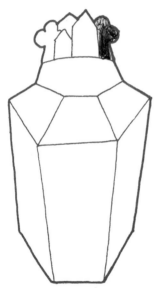

On the Mediterranean Sea in the nation of Lebanon lies the beautiful city of Juniyah. Juniyah's primary asset is its natural setting, a half-bowl of rugged cliffs and forested mountains clutching the shimmering bay like the prongs of a diamond ring. The mountainside is so steep that the view from the cool terrace restaurant near the top is like looking down from the back of a bird. A little higher, in the village of Harissa, 1,700 feet up, a towering statue of the Virgin Mary—"Our Lady of Lebanon"—turns her back on snow-covered peaks and looks down from her conical pedestal as though to bless the 30,000 people in the cluster of hillside villages and the town below. To the west, seemingly at her feet, the waters of the bay ripple toward the sea, changing shades and tones with the passing hours. And to the north and south rocky cliffs extend into the sea, cupping the bay like weathered hands.

1. This paragraph centers on
    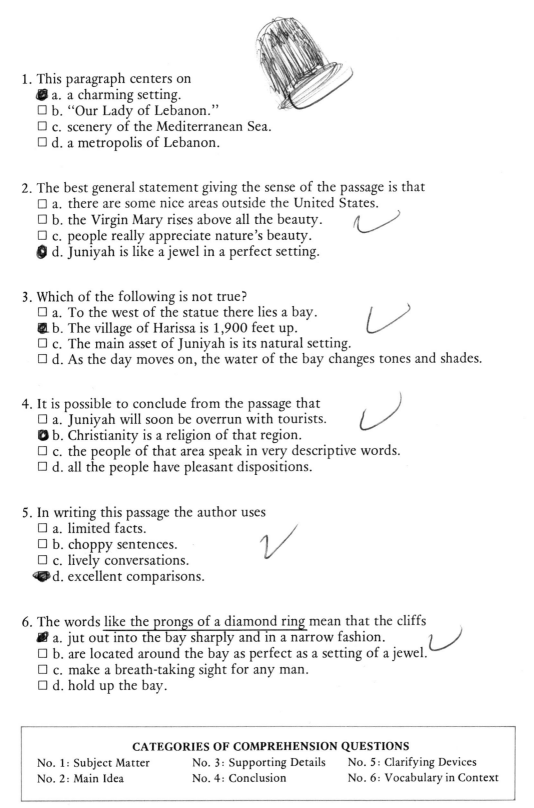
    ☒ a. a charming setting.
    ☐ b. "Our Lady of Lebanon."
    ☐ c. scenery of the Mediterranean Sea.
    ☐ d. a metropolis of Lebanon.

2. The best general statement giving the sense of the passage is that
    ☐ a. there are some nice areas outside the United States.
    ☐ b. the Virgin Mary rises above all the beauty.
    ☐ c. people really appreciate nature's beauty.
    ☒ d. Juniyah is like a jewel in a perfect setting.

3. Which of the following is not true?
    ☐ a. To the west of the statue there lies a bay.
    ☒ b. The village of Harissa is 1,900 feet up.
    ☐ c. The main asset of Juniyah is its natural setting.
    ☐ d. As the day moves on, the water of the bay changes tones and shades.

4. It is possible to conclude from the passage that
    ☐ a. Juniyah will soon be overrun with tourists.
    ☒ b. Christianity is a religion of that region.
    ☐ c. the people of that area speak in very descriptive words.
    ☐ d. all the people have pleasant dispositions.

5. In writing this passage the author uses
    ☐ a. limited facts.
    ☐ b. choppy sentences.
    ☐ c. lively conversations.
    ☒ d. excellent comparisons.

6. The words like the prongs of a diamond ring mean that the cliffs
    ☒ a. jut out into the bay sharply and in a narrow fashion.
    ☐ b. are located around the bay as perfect as a setting of a jewel.
    ☐ c. make a breath-taking sight for any man.
    ☐ d. hold up the bay.

CATEGORIES OF COMPREHENSION QUESTIONS

No. 1: Subject Matter	No. 3: Supporting Details	No. 5: Clarifying Devices
No. 2: Main Idea	No. 4: Conclusion	No. 6: Vocabulary in Context

60. THE CRUSADES WIDEN EUROPE'S HORIZONS

The cross-bearers who went on the long journey to the Middle East from France, England, Germany and Italy knew little of the kind of people they were going to meet there. All they knew was that they were going to try to take sacred territory from the hands of "the Infidels," "unbelievers" whose God and Prophet were different from their own. After once making contact with the East, the crusaders were surprised to find there a highly developed culture which was not only much older than Europe's but in many ways quite superior.

Islam and Christianity had many things in common—most importantly, a belief in one God. The Islamic codes of morality and hospitality deeply impressed the men from the West. At a time when losses from battle and <u>pestilence</u> called for every bit of medical skill available, doctors who accompanied the crusaders discovered that Moslem medicine was far ahead of their own.

1. The best title for this selection would be:
   ☐ a. The Conquest of the Middle East.
   ☐ b. Education of the Crusaders.
   ☐ c. Crusades of Europe.
   ☐ d. Islamic Law and Religion.

2. The crusaders were surprised to discover that Moslem culture was
   ☐ a. less advanced than their own.
   ☐ b. more advanced than their own.
   ☐ c. similar to their own.
   ☐ d. primitive in most respects.

3. The crusaders were called "cross-bearers" because they
   ☐ a. believed in God.
   ☐ b. suffered so greatly.
   ☐ c. were so crude.
   ☐ d. were Christians.

4. We can conclude from the passage that wounded crusaders were
   ☐ a. left to die unaided.
   ☐ b. helped by Moslem medical knowledge.
   ☐ c. cured by their accompanying doctors.
   ☐ d. carried home for medical treatment.

5. The author supports his thesis by
   ☐ a. arguments and proof.
   ☐ b. cause and effect.
   ☐ c. comparison and contrast.
   ☐ d. specific examples.

6. The word pestilence, as used in this passage, is closest in meaning to
   ☐ a. infection.
   ☐ b. wound.
   ☐ c. epidemic disease.
   ☐ d. insect poison.

CATEGORIES OF COMPREHENSION QUESTIONS

| No. 1: Subject Matter | No. 3: Supporting Details | No. 5: Clarifying Devices |
| No. 2: Main Idea | No. 4: Conclusion | No. 6: Vocabulary in Context |

61. THE STORY OF HALLOWEEN

Irish immigrants brought their Halloween customs to the United States in pioneer times. The Halloween celebration first took root as a harvest festival, sometimes called Snap-Apple Night or Nut-Crack Night. It is still called Nut-Crack Night in parts of northern England. In 1840 the Irish potato famine and the emigration that followed spread the full range of Halloween folk customs to most of the United States.

The American custom of trick-or-treat was probably borrowed from an Irish custom of going masked to seek farm produce in honor of Muck Olla, a mythical figure of <u>obscure</u> origin. Many Halloween games were originally Irish fortunetelling tricks. Halloween mischief, harmless and otherwise, traces to the Irish Vigil of Samhain, as the festival is still called in some parts of Ireland. Halloween goblins and fairies were supposed to account for the devilment and soothe the vexations of those whose property had been mishandled.

1. This selection is mainly about
   - ☐ a. the Irish potato famine.
   - ☐ b. the origins of Halloween customs.
   - ☐ c. the first celebration of Halloween in England.
   - ☐ d. Muck Olla, the originator of Halloween.

2. The festival of Halloween is celebrated
   - ☐ a. by a variety of folk customs in the United States.
   - ☐ b. during harvest time in England.
   - ☐ c. by the mishandling of property in Ireland.
   - ☐ d. to honor the emigration of the Irish to the United States.

3. The Irish attributed Halloween mischief to
   - ☐ a. the potato famine.
   - ☐ b. the mythical figure of Muck Olla.
   - ☐ c. goblins and fairies.
   - ☐ d. an innovation of the English.

4. American Halloween customs evolved
   - ☐ a. independently of those practiced in other parts of the world.
   - ☐ b. from Irish fortunetelling tricks.
   - ☐ c. during the potato famine in Ireland.
   - ☐ d. from Irish folk traditions.

5. The last sentence of the passage suggests that
   - ☐ a. it was difficult to account for property damage.
   - ☐ b. people only pretended to accept the myth of goblins and fairies.
   - ☐ c. goblins and fairies may have been responsible for the property damage.
   - ☐ d. the Irish were very superstitious and believed in the supernatural.

6. The word <u>obscure</u>, as used in the passage, means
   - ☐ a. well-known.
   - ☐ b. exact.
   - ☐ c. unclear.
   - ☐ d. ancient.

CATEGORIES OF COMPREHENSION QUESTIONS

No. 1: Subject Matter	No. 3: Supporting Details	No. 5: Clarifying Devices
No. 2: Main Idea	No. 4: Conclusion	No. 6: Vocabulary in Context

62. THE RESOURCE WITH HORNS

 In the Middle East, as in other parts of the world, goats are important elements in the economic structure. Hardy and ubiquitous, able to live off weeds, shrubs, and grass—in short, off vegetation—the goat, like its cousin the sheep, is a major source of several economically valuable products. Its hide produces soft leather. Its long, coarse hair is woven into tough, durable rugs. Its flesh provides a meat so tender that it is a staple of the area, delicious when carved from vertical spits and served with mint, or skewered with tomatoes and onions. In many Middle East suburbs it is a common sight to see herds of nannies clicking stiff-legged through the streets, delivering, right into the jugs and pans of housewives, a daily ration of fresh milk. Goat milk is not only free from any taint of tuberculosis, but also richer in protein and fat than cows' milk and, further, is particularly suitable for the manufacture of a salty white cheese. From the standpoint of the small farmer, goats have an added advantage: they are inexpensive to get and keep.

1. This passage focuses on
   □ a. goats in the Middle East.
   □ b. how goats survive in the suburbs.
   □ c. valuable products from goats.
   □ d. foods that come from goats.

2. The best statement of the main idea of this passage would be that
   □ a. goats thrive in many parts of the world.
   □ b. goats are a valuable economic resource of the Middle East.
   □ c. goat milk is a nourishing food.
   □ d. nutritious meals are made of goat meat.

3. Goat milk is readily obtained by suburban housewives from
   □ a. the goat herders.
   □ b. the goats in the mountains.
   □ c. stores.
   □ d. goats walking through the streets.

4. Goats are shown to be
   □ a. very useful animals.
   □ b. useful, but very destructive.
   □ c. the most important economic resource of the area.
   □ d. delicious when eaten.

5. The author states his main idea in the first sentence and supports it throughout the paragraph by means of
   □ a. contrast.
   □ b. cause and effect.
   □ c. examples.
   □ d. definition.

6. The word ubiquitous means
   □ a. present nearly everywhere.
   □ b. friendly and harmless.
   □ c. intelligent.
   □ d. strong.

CATEGORIES OF COMPREHENSION QUESTIONS		
No. 1: Subject Matter	No. 3: Supporting Details	No. 5: Clarifying Devices
No. 2: Main Idea	No. 4: Conclusion	No. 6: Vocabulary in Context

63. PLAGUE ACROSS THE LAND

The locust is perhaps nature's most awesome example of the collective destructive power of a species which, individually, is practically harmless. An adult locust weighs a maximum of two grams—it takes over 225 to outweigh a can of beans. The destructive power is based on two facts. One, each locust can eat its own weight daily. Two, the moving swarm may carpet the ground with anywhere from 30 to 60 locusts a square yard; therefore, a square mile will typically contain from 100 million to 200 million of the creatures. Seldom, furthermore, will a swarm occupy a mere square mile; swarms more than 400 square miles in area have been recorded. A swarm that size weighs more than 80,000 tons and numbers around 40 billion insects eating the weight of the *Queen Mary* every day it is on the move—and it never stops. As small a number of locusts as one million—two tons of locusts!—takes a tremendous toll and each day eats as much as 20 elephants or 500 people. And their <u>voracity</u> is not only in numbers; pound for pound the locust eats 60 to 100 times as much as a human being.

1. This article is mainly concerned with
   □ a. the harmlessness of individual locusts.
   □ b. the Queen Mary locust plague.
   □ c. the destructive capacity of locusts.
   □ d. the importance of locusts to man.

2. Locusts
   □ a. existed only in the Bible.
   □ b. are extremely destructive in swarms.
   □ c. ate the *Queen Mary* in one day.
   □ d. eat as much as twenty elephants.

3. A locust
   □ a. can fly over long distances.
   □ b. always travels in swarms.
   □ c. is no larger than a bean.
   □ d. can eat its own weight daily.

4. The destructiveness of locusts in swarms results from all of the following except
   □ a. the large area covered by the swarm.
   □ b. the large number of locusts in a swarm.
   □ c. their collective voracity.
   □ d. the extreme weight of a locust swarm.

5. The author uses
   □ a. contrast and comparison.
   □ b. factual description.
   □ c. simile and metaphor.
   □ d. biased opinion.

6. As used in this passage, voracity means
   □ a. having an enormous appetite.
   □ b. habitually tells the truth.
   □ c. possessed of great strength.
   □ d. utterly useless.

CATEGORIES OF COMPREHENSION QUESTIONS		
No. 1: Subject Matter	No. 3: Supporting Details	No. 5: Clarifying Devices
No. 2: Main Idea	No. 4: Conclusion	No. 6: Vocabulary in Context

64. MEDINA—SECOND CITY OF ISLAM

In Medina, the Prophet Muhammad found at last the faith and unshakable support denied him by his own tribe, the Quraish of Mecca. In Medina were revealed to Muhammad the concluding *suras* [chapters] of the Koran, the foundation of the Moslem religion, Islam. In that city, Muhammad planned, and fought nearby, the three decisive battles against his Meccan foes. And from Medina he launched the hosts of believers, ten thousand strong, who awed his opponents into lasting submission. In Medina, Muhammad lived the final decade of his life, and there he died and was buried. From Medina the first three Caliphs, or successors of the Prophet, ruled the Arab empire.

So significant is Muhammad's arrival in Medina from Mecca in 622 A.D. that the chronology of Islam rests upon that single momentous event. The very name Medina, which in Arabic means simply "The City" without further qualification, eloquently attests to its importance. Yet outside Islam, the crucial role it played in the development of a religion whose 45 million followers girdle the earth is all but unknown.

1. This passage is mainly about
   ☐ a. Muslims.
   ☐ b. Islam.
   ☐ c. Medina.
   ☐ d. the Koran.

2. According to the passage, Medina is
   ☐ a. an insignificant city.
   ☐ b. the birthplace of Muhammed.
   ☐ c. an important city in Islamic culture.
   ☐ d. a country in Arabia.

3. Which of the following did not happen to Muhammed in Medina?
   ☐ a. His birth
   ☐ b. The revelation of parts of the Koran
   ☐ c. His death
   ☐ d. Acceptance and belief in his teachings

4. The passage indicates that
   ☐ a. Islam is the world's largest religion.
   ☐ b. Islam was not readily accepted by all.
   ☐ c. Muhammed was the first Caliph.
   ☐ d. Medina is the most important city in the Arab world.

5. What does the author use to support the main idea of this passage?
   ☐ a. Comparison
   ☐ b. Logic
   ☐ c. Facts
   ☐ d. Arguments

6. As used in this passage, <u>chronology</u> refers to
   ☐ a. the classification of events in order of time.
   ☐ b. future success.
   ☐ c. the occurrence of key events.
   ☐ d. the order in which well-timed events occur.

CATEGORIES OF COMPREHENSION QUESTIONS

| No. 1: Subject Matter | No. 3: Supporting Details | No. 5: Clarifying Devices |
| No. 2: Main Idea | No. 4: Conclusion | No. 6: Vocabulary in Context |

65. MAN ON THE MOVE

Although steam power had been used successfully to operate a mill, its potential for propelling vehicles and ships was not realized until 1783. That was the year that a French nobleman, the Marquis d'Abbans, created a steam-driven paddle-wheel vessel that could buck a stiff river current. Twenty years later, America's Robert Fulton launched the first successful steamboat, and by 1807 his famous *Clermont* was puffing up and down the Hudson between New York and Albany.

Steam power won world-wide attention in 1819, when the 100-foot American packet *Savannah* became the first steamship to cross the Atlantic. Even though the *Savannah*'s engine broke down on the homeward voyage, forcing her to rely on her sail power, there was no doubt that steam would henceforth move men across water.

The steamship came into its own when Sir Charles Parsons, an English engineer, perfected an engine that replaced the less efficient pistons with revolving turbines. In 1897, officers of the British navy stood <u>agape</u> at a review in Spithead anchorage while Parsons' experimental ship *Turbina* whisked past them at almost 40 miles per hour.

1. This selection focuses on
   - ☐ a. the steam engine.
   - ☐ b. steam-driven ships.
   - ☐ c. the invention of the turbine.
   - ☐ d. Robert Fulton's inventions.

2. It became clear that steamships would replace sailing ships when
   - ☐ a. Parsons invented the turbine.
   - ☐ b. the *Clermont* steamed up and down the Hudson.
   - ☐ c. the *Savannah* steamed across the Atlantic.
   - ☐ d. the *Turbina* traveled 40 miles per hour.

3. Robert Fulton launched his first successful steamboat in the year
   - ☐ a. 1783.
   - ☐ b. 1803.
   - ☐ c. 1807.
   - ☐ d. 1819.

4. This selection implies that steam power was first used
   - ☐ a. in transportation.
   - ☐ b. in industry.
   - ☐ c. in turbines.
   - ☐ d. for heating.

5. The facts in this passage are presented in order of
   - ☐ a. importance.
   - ☐ b. time.
   - ☐ c. interest.
   - ☐ d. dependence.

6. Men who are <u>agape</u> show the emotion of
   - ☐ a. surprise.
   - ☐ b. fear.
   - ☐ c. anger.
   - ☐ d. boredom.

CATEGORIES OF COMPREHENSION QUESTIONS

No. 1: Subject Matter	No. 3: Supporting Details	No. 5: Clarifying Devices
No. 2: Main Idea	No. 4: Conclusion	No. 6: Vocabulary in Context

66. THE HIGHWAY AND THE CITY

Julius Caesar won fame as general, statesman, and author—but he was also something of a traffic engineer, and not by choice. Traffic snarls were so acute in the marketplace of Imperial Rome and around the Circus Maximus that Caesar was forced to bar all except pedestrian traffic for the ten hours after sunrise. He also found it necessary to institute one-way streets and abolish downtown parking.

Many of today's city traffic woes had their Roman counterparts. Instead of smog, there were clouds of dust and swarms of insects. Instead of auto horns, there were the clatter of horses' hoofs and the roar of chariot wheels on stone pavement. Even the *alleged* modern problem of the woman driver was known to ancient Rome: Lady charioteers were not permitted to drive in the city on Sundays or during times of heavy traffic.

Down through history urban roads have been plagued by these and similar difficulties as men have sought to devise efficient and convenient means of moving people and goods. Roads have always been essential to the growth of the city—roads to bear chariots, horses and buggies, bicycles, and, finally, automobiles, buses and trucks.

1. The passage discusses
   - ☐ a. a historical antecedent of the modern traffic jam.
   - ☐ b. Julius Caesar's importance as a traffic director.
   - ☐ c. ways in which we could reduce traffic congestion.
   - ☐ d. the importance of transportation to the development of a nation.

2. Traffic problems
   - ☐ a. are unique to the 20th century.
   - ☐ b. are often made worse by women drivers.
   - ☐ c. existed as long ago as the days of Julius Caesar.
   - ☐ d. have become considerably more serious with the advent of modern forms of transportation.

3. One measure which Caesar did not impose to alleviate the traffic problem was
   - ☐ a. prohibiting women from driving on Sundays.
   - ☐ b. abolishing downtown parking.
   - ☐ c. instituting one-way streets.
   - ☐ d. banning driving after sundown.

4. The author implies that
   - ☐ a. traffic problems are inevitable and will always exist.
   - ☐ b. traffic problems are not solely a result of the invention of the automobile.
   - ☐ c. women have always been known to be worse drivers than men.
   - ☐ d. few people have understood the relationship between roads and growth of cities.

5. By putting the word *"alleged"* in italics, the author shows that
   - ☐ a. many so-called knowledgeable people have falsely attacked women.
   - ☐ b. many people object to women driving at all.
   - ☐ c. most people blame women for most serious accidents.
   - ☐ d. women have not been proven to be a source of traffic problems.

6. Something which is *alleged* is
   - ☐ a. asserted but not proven.
   - ☐ b. a commonly held false assumption.
   - ☐ c. done out of a sense of helpfulness or duty.
   - ☐ d. said or done for a dubious purpose.

CATEGORIES OF COMPREHENSION QUESTIONS

No. 1: Subject Matter	No. 3: Supporting Details	No. 5: Clarifying Devices
No. 2: Main Idea	No. 4: Conclusion	No. 6: Vocabulary in Context

67. THE ARABIAN HORSE

The bones of an Arabian horse are <u>as dense as ivory</u> and he has many fewer leg problems than most other breeds, particularly such highbred types as the Thoroughbred. In 300-mile endurance rides conducted by the U.S. Remount Service in the 1920s, only 15 percent of the pure Arabians developed leg problems compared to 90 percent of the pure Thoroughbreds. Because his bones are so strong, and because he has a relatively short back (one vertebra less than other horses), he can carry more weight per pound, and for longer distances, than any other horse. This was also demonstrated in the Remount Service's endurance tests. After five days over rough country, carrying heavy weights, many showed hardly any fatigue at all.

"The Arabian's ability to function, as well as his beauty, comes from the way he is put together," says Gerald Donoghue, president of the Arabian Horse Owners' Foundation and a long-time breeder himself. "He is perfectly proportioned, nothing in excess, no one part of him extreme in relation to any other. He is built for action. His legs, flaring nostrils, the set of his neck, and rib cage all give him the capacity to run for incredibly long distances without getting winded."

1. This selection centers on the Arabian horse's
   - ☐ a. healthy disposition.
   - ☐ b. physical build.
   - ☐ c. character traits.
   - ☐ d. strong bone structure.

2. The purpose of this passage is to
   - ☐ a. show that Arabians are better than Thoroughbreds.
   - ☐ b. explain why Arabians run fast.
   - ☐ c. interest the reader in horse racing.
   - ☐ d. give the reader a better understanding of the Arabian horse.

3. The Arabian horse is *not*
   - ☐ a. large.
   - ☐ b. functional.
   - ☐ c. strong.
   - ☐ d. beautiful.

4. The Arabian is admired for its
   - ☐ a. gentleness.
   - ☐ b. rarity.
   - ☐ c. perfection.
   - ☐ d. intelligence.

5. The author quotes Gerald Donoghue in order to present
   - ☐ a. a different point of view.
   - ☐ b. an objective opinion.
   - ☐ c. a personal story.
   - ☐ d. an expert's opinion.

6. By saying that the Arabian's bones are as dense as ivory, the author implies that the bones are
   - ☐ a. soft and flexible.
   - ☐ b. compact and strong.
   - ☐ c. light and brittle.
   - ☐ d. pure and fine.

CATEGORIES OF COMPREHENSION QUESTIONS

No. 1: Subject Matter	No. 3: Supporting Details	No. 5: Clarifying Devices
No. 2: Main Idea	No. 4: Conclusion	No. 6: Vocabulary in Context

68. THE NIGHT BEFORE THE REVOLUTION

Until Longfellow wrote his poem "Paul Revere's Ride," in 1860, Revere's stirring feat was remembered only in Boston and then somewhat vaguely. Although Longfellow helped to make Revere a national hero, the venerable poet took many liberties with the facts. The last stanza ("It was two by the village clock when he came to the bridge in Concord town...") is fiction. Revere never made it to Concord that night.

After leaving Lexington, Revere and Dawes picked up another rider, Dr. Sam Prescott, a Concord resident who was returning home from an evening spent courting a Lexington girl. Prescott, also a revolutionary, sped on with Revere and Dawes.

Then, some two miles beyond Lexington, another British patrol materialized from the shadows, halted the riders and arrested them. Dr. Prescott escaped by jumping his horse over a stone wall and was able to deliver the news to Concord. Revere and Dawes were held in custody for an hour or so and then released— but not before a British trooper had "confiscated" Revere's horse. Presumably the gallant little animal that had carried Revere ended his days in the service of the King. But the King's days in America were already numbered.

1. The best title for this selection would be:
   - ☐ a. Sam Prescott's Ride.
   - ☐ b. Paul Revere's Ride.
   - ☐ c. Correcting a Legend.
   - ☐ d. The Venerable Poet Longfellow.

2. Longfellow's version is incorrect because
   - ☐ a. Revere did not reach Concord.
   - ☐ b. Prescott was captured.
   - ☐ c. Revere was a hero.
   - ☐ d. Revere was courting a Lexington girl.

3. The man who actually delivered the news to Concord was
   - ☐ a. Revere.
   - ☐ b. Dawes.
   - ☐ c. Longfellow.
   - ☐ d. Prescott.

4. Longfellow's poem states that
   - ☐ a. Dawes was a hero.
   - ☐ b. another rider reached Concord.
   - ☐ c. Prescott was a coward.
   - ☐ d. Revere reached Concord.

5. The author assumes that his reader is familiar with
   - ☐ a. Revere's ride.
   - ☐ b. the causes of the Revolution.
   - ☐ c. the geography of Massachusetts.
   - ☐ d. the true facts of the incident.

6. As used in this passage, materialized seems to mean
   - ☐ a. brought in useful material.
   - ☐ b. appeared suddenly.
   - ☐ c. destroyed valuable material.
   - ☐ d. provided material for a story.

CATEGORIES OF COMPREHENSION QUESTIONS

| No. 1: Subject Matter | No. 3: Supporting Details | No. 5: Clarifying Devices |
| No. 2: Main Idea | No. 4: Conclusion | No. 6: Vocabulary in Context |

69. CEDARS KEPT LEBANON IN PLACE

Driving in the Lebanese mountains after a winter cloudburst, one can look down on the coast and see a graphic example of the effects of erosion—brown rain water rushing into the blue sea. The water is brown because it carries with it great quantities of soil carried away by torrents that churn down the slopes in swift streams and rivulets. In the mountains themselves there is on every hand equally clear evidence of the effects of erosion. Gullies and valleys have been gouged into the soft limestone cliffs where wind and rain have already worn away the thin but vital cover of vegetation.

The Lebanese mountains were not always this vulnerable. In ancient days, Lebanese cedars, those sturdy monarchs among trees, spread their graceful horizontal caps across the slopes in great forests that covered more than 650 thousand acres. Joining their deep strong roots to the web of smaller roots and root hairs extending from the myriad grasses and shrubs below, the great trees kept a tight, protective hold upon the soil. Through the centuries, however, the great trees fell victim to the need and greed of Egyptian pharaohs, Levantine kings, Roman emperors and Turkish sultans, until, in the nineteenth century, Queen Victoria of England dispatched funds to build a wall around the pitiful remnants—a small grove of some 400 trees—to preserve them from extinction. As the trees vanished, the grasses and shrubs, deprived of their protection, gave way too. Soil followed as it always does when nature's delicate ecological structure is thrown out of balance.

1. This selection deals mainly with Lebanon and the problem of
   - ☐ a. mountain erosion.
   - ☐ b. cedar preservation.
   - ☐ c. cloudbursts.
   - ☐ d. its former rulers.

2. There was less erosion in ancient days because there were
   - ☐ a. more trees.
   - ☐ b. more grasses and shrubs.
   - ☐ c. fewer cloudbursts.
   - ☐ d. protective walls.

3. The decrease in the amount of trees was due to
   - ☐ a. erosion by wind and rain.
   - ☐ b. crowding by grasses and shrubs.
   - ☐ c. a decree by Queen Victoria.
   - ☐ d. the need and greed of ancient rulers.

4. One result of erosion is the
   - ☐ a. desertion of the affected area.
   - ☐ b. filling in of valleys.
   - ☐ c. stripping of the soil.
   - ☐ d. imbalance of nature.

5. The function of the first paragraph in relation to the second is
   - ☐ a. to introduce the subject.
   - ☐ b. to illustrate a point.
   - ☐ c. to arouse keen interest.
   - ☐ d. to summarize.

6. The best synonym for myriad in this passage would be
   - ☐ a. thick.
   - ☐ b. tall.
   - ☐ c. countless.
   - ☐ d. network.

CATEGORIES OF COMPREHENSION QUESTIONS

| No. 1: Subject Matter | No. 3: Supporting Details | No. 5: Clarifying Devices |
| No. 2: Main Idea | No. 4: Conclusion | No. 6: Vocabulary in Context |

70. THE TELEGRAM

Telegraphy was introduced in 1837 by an American artist, Samuel Morse. Morse, experimenting with magnets, showed President Van Buren that he could tap a telegraph key and send a coded impulse over a wire. The impulse could produce a visible mark and an audible "click" on the other end of the wire, where a magnet set a stylus and a "sounding bar" in action. An experimental line soon was built from Washington to Baltimore. It was over this line, in 1844, that Morse sent his triumphant telegram: "What hath God wrought!"

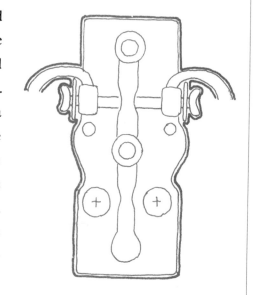

1. This passage centers on
   □ a. Samuel Morse and President Van Buren.
   □ b. the experimental line built from Washington to Baltimore.
   □ c. Samuel Morse's invention of the telegraph.
   □ d. the use of telegraphy in religion.

2. According to the paragraph
   □ a. the telegraph was first invented in the eighteenth century.
   □ b. Samuel Morse's experiments with magnets led to the basic method of sending telegrams.
   □ c. President Van Buren was aware of and fully impressed with telegraphy.
   □ d. the line between Baltimore and Washington carried the only telegram Morse sent.

3. The telegraph key mentioned in the passage
   □ a. would make a visible mark and audible click.
   □ b. could continuously pick up coded impulses over the wire.
   □ c. was very similar to the key of a typewriter today.
   □ d. sent impulses over the telegraph line.

4. Which of the following conclusions could you draw from the passage?
   □ a. The experimental line became the world's largest private telegraph network.
   □ b. Other telegraph lines sprang up after the experimental one was successful.
   □ c. President Van Buren gave Samuel Morse a large grant for his work.
   □ d. Many people began to send telegrams to relatives who lived far away.

5. In the passage which of the techniques listed below is used?
   □ a. Compiling experimental data
   □ b. Citing an historical account
   □ c. Supporting the main idea with many details
   □ d. Making comparisons

6. Which expression below is closest to the meaning of the phrase, "What hath God wrought"?
   □ a. Observe what God has accomplished!
   □ b. I don't believe the whole thing.
   □ c. Why are we so fortunate?
   □ d. God will bless this invention!

CATEGORIES OF COMPREHENSION QUESTIONS

No. 1: Subject Matter	No. 3: Supporting Details	No. 5: Clarifying Devices
No. 2: Main Idea	No. 4: Conclusion	No. 6: Vocabulary in Context

71. THE SARI

Six yards of material, simply
and deftly draped by the wearer,
make one of the most becoming
and graceful garments any woman
can wear. Called a sari, it is as
timeless as the country of its
origin, India, and is impervious
to the whims and dictates of
Western fashion. Soft cottons,
gay prints, gauzy silks woven with
patterns of gold or silver—the
material varies the formality of
the sari—but never the basic design. A long skirt, softly pleated
in front, is draped across the
back, and continues in a length
of cloth slung over one shoulder,
carried over the arm, or covering
the head, as the wearer's tastes
dictate.

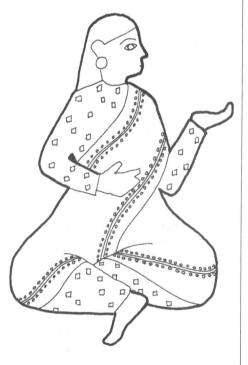

1. The passage deals mostly with
   - ☐ a. six yards of material.
   - ☐ b. Indian costumes.
   - ☐ c. methods of wearing a sari.
   - ☐ d. the sari.

2. The main purpose of this passage is to give the reader information
   - ☐ a. about the different types of saris.
   - ☐ b. on how to wrap a sari.
   - ☐ c. of the general features of the sari.
   - ☐ d. and to encourage him to wear the sari.

3. Which of the following is not true?
   - ☐ a. The basic design of the long skirt may vary.
   - ☐ b. The sari originated in India.
   - ☐ c. For a very long time the sari has been in existence.
   - ☐ d. Approximately six yards of material are needed to make a sari.

4. It appears from the passage that the sari
   - ☐ a. has either gold or silver woven into it for special occasions.
   - ☐ b. must be worn in a particular manner.
   - ☐ c. costs more than the average dress.
   - ☐ d. is worn only by Indian women who choose to ignore Western dress.

5. In the paragraph the author employs all of the following except
   - ☐ a. expressive words.
   - ☐ b. general description.
   - ☐ c. arguments and proof.
   - ☐ d. interesting details.

6. As used in this passage, impervious to seems to mean
   - ☐ a. changeable according to.
   - ☐ b. not responsive to.
   - ☐ c. copied by.
   - ☐ d. an imitation of.

CATEGORIES OF COMPREHENSION QUESTIONS

No. 1: Subject Matter	No. 3: Supporting Details	No. 5: Clarifying Devices
No. 2: Main Idea	No. 4: Conclusion	No. 6: Vocabulary in Context

72. THE ALLIGATOR

Compared to his wild, aggressive cousins, the crocodiles, the
American alligator is a gentleman
towards people, even though it
can roar and hiss—and look—
like a dragon. In captivity, the
alligator, unlike the peevish crocodile, seems to ignore humans or
even regard them with amused
tolerance. A relaxed alligator
seen in profile appears to be
grinning.

At Florida alligator "farms,"
where its tough appearance makes
tourists shudder, it even submits
to wrestling. A strong young man
will tussle one out of a pond and
onto a float by first throwing it
on its back and then gently mas-
saging its belly until the 'gator is
"hypnotised," and goes limp. No
crocodile would stand for such
treatment.

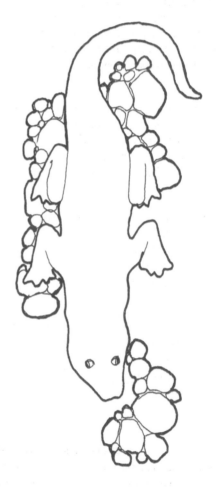

1. This passage is mainly about
   □ a. the dangerous crocodile.
   □ b. the indifferent alligator.
   □ c. alligator wrestling.
   □ d. alligators in the wild.

2. The alligator can be described as being
   □ a. a vicious man-eater.
   □ b. fearful of humans.
   □ c. mild-mannered, despite his appearance.
   □ d. unresponsive to human attempts to annoy him.

3. By rubbing its belly one can
   □ a. enrage a crocodile.
   □ b. capture a wild crocodile.
   □ c. stimulate an alligator to wrestle.
   □ d. calm an alligator.

4. Unlike the crocodile, the alligator
   □ a. cannot be hypnotized.
   □ b. tolerates humans.
   □ c. has a tough appearance.
   □ d. can live in captivity.

5. The author develops his point by using
   □ a. narration.
   □ b. analogy.
   □ c. contrast.
   □ d. comparison.

6. The word peevish, as used in the passage, means
   □ a. irritable.
   □ b. curious.
   □ c. fierce.
   □ d. cunning.

CATEGORIES OF COMPREHENSION QUESTIONS

| No. 1: Subject Matter | No. 3: Supporting Details | No. 5: Clarifying Devices |
| No. 2: Main Idea | No. 4: Conclusion | No. 6: Vocabulary in Context |

73. THE THUNDERHEAD

When nimbus and cumulus clouds get together, nature stages one of her most masterful melodramas—starring the *cumulonimbus* or "thunderhead." The thunderhead, the prima donna of all the rain clouds, is a turbulent, anvil-shaped mass of wind and water vapor often five or six miles tall. Blue, green, black, and purple towers rise and fall within it, illuminated by streaks of lightning. At its base, dark grape-like clusters of clouds boil and bubble, and in certain sections of the world, particularly the midwestern United States, these clusters foreshadow the birth of the most villainous of all storms: the tornado.

1. This passage centers on
   ☐ a. nimbus and cumulus clouds.
   ☐ b. the color of storm clouds.
   ☐ c. storms and lightning.
   ☐ d. the thunderhead cloud.

2. The best general statement giving the sense of this passage is that
   ☐ a. the cumulonimbus cloud is very turbulent.
   ☐ b. different clouds combine easily.
   ☐ c. the most villainous of all storms is the tornado.
   ☐ d. the cumulonimbus cloud is composed of wind and water vapor.

3. This passage does not say that the cumulonimbus cloud is
   ☐ a. a combination of cumulus and nimbus clouds.
   ☐ b. as dangerous as the tornado.
   ☐ c. full of blue, green, black and purple towers.
   ☐ d. often five or six miles tall.

4. We can infer from this passage that tornadoes
   ☐ a. are more frequent in Arizona than California.
   ☐ b. are extremely dangerous.
   ☐ c. produce a lot of lightning.
   ☐ d. are a direct result of rain cloud clusters.

5. The author develops his point in the passage through the use of
   ☐ a. arguments.
   ☐ b. comparison.
   ☐ c. contrast.
   ☐ d. facts.

6. The word turbulent means
   ☐ a. violently agitated.
   ☐ b. terribly destructive.
   ☐ c. dense.
   ☐ d. boiling.

CATEGORIES OF COMPREHENSION QUESTIONS		
No. 1: Subject Matter	No. 3: Supporting Details	No. 5: Clarifying Devices
No. 2: Main Idea	No. 4: Conclusion	No. 6: Vocabulary in Context

74. LIFE AMONG THE CORAL

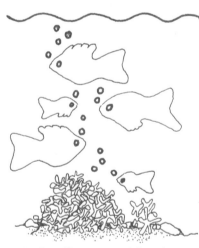 Coral reefs teem with fish of every sort: the stately angelfish; the smaller, more brightly-hued butterfly fish; parrot fish loudly colored in wild schemes of yellows, pinks, greens, blacks; countless schools of ocean fish, some nearly transparent, others reflecting light off their bodies like tiny mirrors. Amid this flurry of color and activity lies a slow-moving grouper basking in the sun.

As in all communities, however, there are deadly elements too. There is the ornate, delicately colored zebra fish, confident in its possession of 21 deadly spines. The antisocial moray eel waits in its hole for a victim, its powerful jaws working slowly. <u>Inoffensive</u> stingrays flap their winglike bodies as they drift through coral canyons apparently unaware of the lethal barb at the base of their whiplike tails.

1. The best title for this selection is:
   □ a. Rainbow Menagerie.
   □ b. Reef Dwellers.
   □ c. Variety under the Sea
   □ d. The Reef: Lovely but Lethal.

2. The main thought of the passage is that
   □ a. fish on the reef present many contrasts.
   □ b. dangers in the reef are often disguised.
   □ c. many reef animals enjoy a peaceful existence.
   □ d. it takes a trained eye to appreciate the reef.

3. According to the passage, the zebra fish is equipped with
   □ a. a barbed tail.
   □ b. powerful jaws.
   □ c. poisonous spines.
   □ d. rich markings.

4. The author of this selection is
   □ a. fascinated.
   □ b. disturbed.
   □ c. confused.
   □ d. curious.

5. The author cites "the slow-moving grouper" in order to provide a
   □ a. point of reference.
   □ b. contrast.
   □ c. comic relief.
   □ d. different outlook.

6. When the author calls stingrays <u>inoffensive</u>, he means they are not
   □ a. harmful.
   □ b. ominous.
   □ c. brave.
   □ d. aggressive.

CATEGORIES OF COMPREHENSION QUESTIONS		
No. 1: Subject Matter	No. 3: Supporting Details	No. 5: Clarifying Devices
No. 2: Main Idea	No. 4: Conclusion	No. 6: Vocabulary in Context

75. LEMONS

The birthplace of the lemon, together with other members of the citrus family, is generally believed to be Cochin-China. From there it spread into the Malaysian islands and India. The Arabs brought citrus fruits into Arabia from India in the ninth century, taking them from Oman to Palestine and Egypt in the tenth century. The word "lemon," although it came into English from the Arabic *leimun,* is of Malay origin. All citrus fruits are designated by the Malays as *lemoen.* This word existed among the Malays long before the Portuguese had doubled the Cape of Good Hope in 1497, and also before the Arabs began their trade with the archipelago. The Crusaders are said to have brought the lemon to Europe. Columbus stopped off at the Canary Islands to pick up some lemon seeds which he later planted in the New World.

1. The passage is mainly about the
   ☐ a. planting of lemons.
   ☐ b. origin of the lemon.
   ☐ c. many ways to spell "lemon."
   ☐ d. Malays and their lemons.

2. The best general statement giving the sense of this passage is that
   ☐ a. lemons are a Malaysian fruit.
   ☐ b. the lemon is a fruit which originated in China.
   ☐ c. since its first growth in Cochin-China the lemon has been passed throughout the world.
   ☐ d. the Crusaders are said to have brought the lemon to Europe

3. Which of the following is not stated in the paragraph?
   ☐ a. Arabs really didn't care for lemons and passed them on to other races.
   ☐ b. The Crusaders did bring the lemon to Europe.
   ☐ c. The word "lemon" is thought to be of Malay origin.
   ☐ d. "Lemon" originated from the Arabic word "leimun."

4. After reading the passage, the reader may possibly conclude
   ☐ a. that tea was popular in China because of the lemon.
   ☐ b. citrus fruits must grow readily in several Asian countries.
   ☐ c. when we think of lemons we should think of lemon meringue pie.
   ☐ d. lemoen means "lemon" in English.

5. In developing the paragraph the author uses
   ☐ a. complicated words.
   ☐ b. analogies.
   ☐ c. logical order of development.
   ☐ d. numerous comparisons.

6. An archipelago is
   ☐ a. a group of small islands.
   ☐ b. a peninsula.
   ☐ c. the peak of a mountain.
   ☐ d. a deep and dark body of water.

CATEGORIES OF COMPREHENSION QUESTIONS		
No. 1: Subject Matter	No. 3: Supporting Details	No. 5: Clarifying Devices
No. 2: Main Idea	No. 4: Conclusion	No. 6: Vocabulary in Context

76. WINDMILLS OF EUROPE

Windmills were brought to Europe late in the 12th century by knights returning from the Third Crusade. This implies an Eastern origin. Beyond that, records are contradictory. For instance, Hero of Alexandria, writing in the first century B.C., credits himself with inventing the windmill. However, a Hindu writer three centuries earlier described water being raised by "contrivances worked by wind power."

Despite its vague beginning, the windmill took root in Europe. It ground flour, pumped water and powered light industry right up to the Industrial Revolution. It was, and always has been, the essence of simplicity. Its mechanics are fundamental. The wind revolves the sails which turn what is called the wind shaft. The torque, or twisting force, created in the shaft is then transmitted, through a series of gears, to the grindstone, the pump, the loom or the wood saw.

1. The best title for this selection would be:
   □ a. The Origin of Windmills.
   □ b. The Use of Wind Power.
   □ c. The Distribution of Windmills.
   □ d. Windmills of America.

2. The moving sails of the windmill create
   □ a. electric power.
   □ b. twisting force.
   □ c. stored energy.
   □ d. wind currents.

3. The author says that the windmill supplied power for
   □ a. making electricity.
   □ b. mining coal.
   □ c. operating machinery.
   □ d. sailboats.

4. The best explanation to the contradiction in the first paragraph would be that
   □ a. neither writer was correct.
   □ b. windmills were invented several times.
   □ c. Hero of Alexandria read Hindu writers.
   □ d. windmills were invented in Europe.

5. When the author says "Windmills were brought to Europe," he means
   □ a. actual windmills were transported.
   □ b. the idea and design were carried.
   □ c. windmills were invented.
   □ d. windmills were exported.

6. As used in this passage, vague seems to mean
   □ a. popular.
   □ b. uncertain.
   □ c. primitive.
   □ d. early.

CATEGORIES OF COMPREHENSION QUESTIONS

| No. 1: Subject Matter | No. 3: Supporting Details | No. 5: Clarifying Devices |
| No. 2: Main Idea | No. 4: Conclusion | No. 6: Vocabulary in Context |

77. VACCINES

Producing vaccines is a painstaking process. Typical of egg vaccine production is the procedure for influenza vaccine in which four strains of virus are raised and <u>modified</u> separately, then mixed together.

Production of the vaccine starts with the incubation of eggs for 11 days until the chick embryos have formed. Eggs containing healthy embryos are disinfected with iodine, then punctured with a drill. A solution containing one of the strains of virus is injected, after which the puncture is sealed.

Eggs are then returned to the incubator for 48 hours, after which they are again inspected. Those in which the embryos are still alive are chilled before being "harvested." A portion of the shell is burned away and the virus-laden fluid is siphoned into sterile containers and rechilled. Then the virus is separated from the egg fluid in a centrifuge machine.

The virus is next placed in a chemical solution which inactivates it; then it is chilled again and inspected for sterility. Only after all this can it be combined in a solution with the other virus strains to create influenza vaccine.

1. This passage centers on the
   ☐ a. fight against the influenza virus.
   ☐ b. production of vaccines.
   ☐ c. process of egg incubation.
   ☐ d. transformation of embryo to vaccine.

2. The characteristic of the vaccine that is emphasized most is its
   ☐ a. slow and complex process of production.
   ☐ b. dependence on the chick embryo.
   ☐ c. use in fighting influenza.
   ☐ d. immunizing effect.

3. After the eggs have been in the incubator for a second time they are
   ☐ a. all "harvested."
   ☐ b. placed in the incubator once again.
   ☐ c. sterilized to kill more germs.
   ☐ d. checked for live embryos.

4. We can conclude after reading this passage that
   ☐ a. vaccination shots are extremely expensive.
   ☐ b. precision and patience are a must in order to produce a vaccine.
   ☐ c. the chick embryo is necessary to the cultivation of all vaccines.
   ☐ d. only a small amount of vaccine may be produced at one time.

5. To develop his main idea, the author uses
   ☐ a. comparison and contrast.
   ☐ b. negative arguments.
   ☐ c. cause and effect.
   ☐ d. detailed explanation.

6. The word modified, as used in the passage, means
   ☐ a. made sterile.
   ☐ b. refined.
   ☐ c. incubated.
   ☐ d. partially altered.

CATEGORIES OF COMPREHENSION QUESTIONS

No. 1: Subject Matter	No. 3: Supporting Details	No. 5: Clarifying Devices
No. 2: Main Idea	No. 4: Conclusion	No. 6: Vocabulary in Context

78. MASTERPIECES ON ASSIGNMENT

For thirty years, Joseph Haydn, son of a wagoner, lived as court musician to Prince Nicholas Esterhazy, a Hungarian nobleman. He was called upon for daily concerts and many operas and was exceedingly happy to turn out for three decades an almost endless succession of compositions to fill the demand. Far from feeling enslaved, he looked upon himself as a very fortunate person until the Prince's death in 1790. After that he signed a contract with a manager, Johann Peter Salomon, and came to London to write six new symphonies. Thus at the age of 60 he undertook the first extensive voyage of his life and was a great success in London. There, between March and May of 1791, he wrote not only the six new symphonies (among his greatest), but also string quartets, orchestral <u>suites</u>, a trio, a cantata and many songs! Three years later, Salomon induced him to come to London again and contracted for six more symphonies. Like many of the world's greatest creators, Haydn was a simple, gentle, methodical and industrious man who rejoiced in his steady employment and was very much loved by those who knew him.

1. The best title for this selection would be:
   - ☐ a. The History of Hungarian Folk Music.
   - ☐ b. Joseph Haydn's Early Years.
   - ☐ c. Haydn: The Industrious Artist.
   - ☐ d. The Temperamental Composer.

2. The aspect of Haydn's career on which this paragraph focuses is his
   - ☐ a. inspirations.
   - ☐ b. travels.
   - ☐ c. productivity.
   - ☐ d. rebellion.

3. Haydn's first work in London was done in
   - ☐ a. 1760.
   - ☐ b. 1771.
   - ☐ c. 1780.
   - ☐ d. 1791.

4. The author suggests that his reader may consider composers who write music to order
   - ☐ a. inspired.
   - ☐ b. enslaved.
   - ☐ c. creative.
   - ☐ d. fortunate.

5. Most of the writing in this paragraph is
   - ☐ a. descriptive.
   - ☐ b. narrative.
   - ☐ c. explanatory.
   - ☐ d. argumentative.

6. In this passage, suites refer to
   - ☐ a. furniture groupings.
   - ☐ b. musical pieces.
   - ☐ c. musicians' dress.
   - ☐ d. simple songs.

CATEGORIES OF COMPREHENSION QUESTIONS

| No. 1: Subject Matter | No. 3: Supporting Details | No. 5: Clarifying Devices |
| No. 2: Main Idea | No. 4: Conclusion | No. 6: Vocabulary in Context |

79. BOATBUILDING ON THE NILE

Because papyrus reeds grew in profusion along the banks of the Nile, the early Egyptians made boats by tying together three bundles of reeds lengthwise, using one bundle as a keel and the other two as sides.

With no similar wealth of reeds available to the Mesopotamian fisherman, his inventiveness was prompted by other objects that floated down the great river. He observed that drowned goats and other animals floated high in the water because of gas inflation. With strips of palm leaf as thread, he sewed goat skins together to form airtight bags and <u>inflated</u> them by blowing air into them. This principle of employing air to push water aside enables man to float at ease and is the same basic principle used in today's wooden racing yachts, steel-hulled passenger ships, and nuclear-powered submarines.

Although the Egyptian boatbuilder eventually began to employ wood in his craft, his wooden vessels were, for a long time, based on the early reed design. Mesopotamian progress consisted of forming a framework of local woods and strapping underneath it a number of inflated skins. Such rafts were capable of carrying extremely heavy loads.

1. This selection deals mainly with
   - ☐ a. the origin of modern boats.
   - ☐ b. the design of primitive boats.
   - ☐ c. the operating principle of boats.
   - ☐ d. the differences in Mesopotamian and Egyptian cultures.

2. The author's main idea is that Egyptians and Mesopotamians
   - ☐ a. were the first people to build boats.
   - ☐ b. devised different ways of constructing boats.
   - ☐ c. became the world's first mariners.
   - ☐ d. understood modern scientific principles.

3. Animal skins provide flotation only if they
   - ☐ a. are from drowned animals.
   - ☐ b. enclose air.
   - ☐ c. are sewn together.
   - ☐ d. have a wooden framework.

4. The way in which people built boats depended upon
   - ☐ a. prevailing technology.
   - ☐ b. the intended purpose.
   - ☐ c. the materials available.
   - ☐ d. absolute standards.

5. In this passage the boats of the Egyptians and Mesopotamians are
   - ☐ a. compared.
   - ☐ b. analyzed.
   - ☐ c. criticized.
   - ☐ d. belittled.

6. The word inflated, as it is used in this selection, means
   - ☐ a. stretched.
   - ☐ b. expanded.
   - ☐ c. pressed flat.
   - ☐ d. treated.

CATEGORIES OF COMPREHENSION QUESTIONS

No. 1: Subject Matter	No. 3: Supporting Details	No. 5: Clarifying Devices
No. 2: Main Idea	No. 4: Conclusion	No. 6: Vocabulary in Context

80. A VISIT TO AN EARLY CITY

Archaeologists recently excavated an early farming village in Northern Iraq dating back to between 7,000 and 6,500 B.C. The village, Jarmo, was a permanent year-round settlement containing about two dozen mud-walled houses.

Jarmo was a little over three acres in size and had about 150 people. No doubt the citizens of Jarmo hunted and gathered food as did their forefathers, but they had other interests as well. Pottery, woven baskets, and rugs, and clay figurines of fertility goddesses found at the site indicate they had religion and crafts and had learned to share ideas.

As these early people learned more about farming, they began looking for level ground where water was more plentiful, and about 5,000 B.C. they discovered the rich land between the Tigris and Euphrates Rivers. Thus Mesopotamia, "the land between the rivers," was born.

During the next thousand years, another development took place. The excellent climate, rich soil and better farming methods made food so plentiful that not everyone had to be a farmer in order to eat. Some began to make things that other people needed, in exchange for food. From this simple farming community came the city as we think of it today—a place where men work at trades, producing what others need in return for what they themselves need.

1. The best title for this selection would be:
   - ☐ a. The Forerunner of the City.
   - ☐ b. The Birth of Civilization.
   - ☐ c. An Early Mountain Village.
   - ☐ d. The Land Between the Rivers.

2. The author's main idea is that the city as we think of it today
   - ☐ a. arose when some men began to make things for others.
   - ☐ b. grew between two rivers.
   - ☐ c. developed because people wanted to be near one another.
   - ☐ d. was occupied by unsuccessful farmers.

3. Which one of these details supports the main idea?
   - ☐ a. The village excavated dates from 6,000 to 5,500 B.C.
   - ☐ b. Early cities were very small.
   - ☐ c. City dwellers still hunted and raised their own food.
   - ☐ d. Highly successful farming conditions and methods existed.

4. It is unlikely that a city would arise in a place where
   - ☐ a. there were steep hills.
   - ☐ b. ample supplies of food were unavailable.
   - ☐ c. there were extremes of temperature.
   - ☐ d. there were no tradesmen.

5. The village of Jarmo is described because it is an example of
   - ☐ a. one of the first cities.
   - ☐ b. the prototype of the city.
   - ☐ c. a permanent community.
   - ☐ d. primitive Mesopotamian religious systems.

6. As used in this passage, figurine seems to mean a
   - ☐ a. small statue.
   - ☐ b. pottery bowl.
   - ☐ c. clay tablet.
   - ☐ d. religious offering.

CATEGORIES OF COMPREHENSION QUESTIONS

No. 1: Subject Matter	No. 3: Supporting Details	No. 5: Clarifying Devices
No. 2: Main Idea	No. 4: Conclusion	No. 6: Vocabulary in Context

81. FABULOUS FUNGUS

Scientists estimate that there are somewhere in the neighborhood of 38,000 varieties of mushrooms. Of these, more than 700 have proven highly edible. For practical purposes, wild mushrooms break down into several categories: dangerously poisonous, slightly poisonous, disagreeable in taste, edible but of mediocre taste, and those of excellent flavor.

Just as their fungus cousins—the blights, rots, rusts, and smuts—mushrooms too, are simple-structured and live off food already prepared by higher forms of plants. The one thing that all fungi lack is the green coloring (chlorophyll) by which green plants, with the sun's help, manufacture their own food.

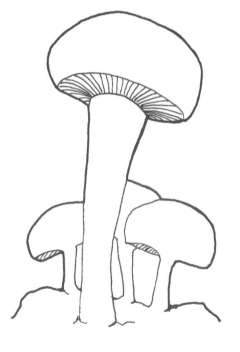

1. This passage is mostly about the
   - ☐ a. structure and varieties of wild mushrooms.
   - ☐ b. history of wild mushrooms.
   - ☐ c. growing of wild mushrooms in the laboratory.
   - ☐ d. usefulness of wild mushrooms.

2. The main idea of this paragraph is that
   - ☐ a. there are many varieties of mushrooms.
   - ☐ b. most wild mushrooms are poisonous.
   - ☐ c. mushrooms are similar to green plants.
   - ☐ d. green plants are more flavorful than mushrooms.

3. Mushrooms are similar to their fungus cousins because they both
   - ☐ a. are very poisonous.
   - ☐ b. manufacture their own food.
   - ☐ c. have the same number of varieties.
   - ☐ d. are simple-structured.

4. Your chances of picking a mushroom of excellent flavor would be
   - ☐ a. 100 percent.
   - ☐ b. 80 percent.
   - ☐ c. 50 percent.
   - ☐ d. 20 percent.

5. The author develops his passage by means of
   - ☐ a. comparison.
   - ☐ b. definition.
   - ☐ c. description.
   - ☐ d. examples.

6. The word <u>mediocre</u>, as used in this passage, means
   - ☐ a. indistinct.
   - ☐ b. barely agreeable.
   - ☐ c. neither good nor bad.
   - ☐ d. bitter.

CATEGORIES OF COMPREHENSION QUESTIONS		
No. 1: Subject Matter	No. 3: Supporting Details	No. 5: Clarifying Devices
No. 2: Main Idea	No. 4: Conclusion	No. 6: Vocabulary in Context

82. PADDLING TO DAMASCUS

Millions of travelers have visited Damascus over the years, but not many have arrived by boat. One who did was John MacGregor, a Scotsman who, just over 100 years ago, sailed his canoe, the "Rob Roy," down the Barada River from its source in the mountains, paddled right across Damascus, and ended his journey in a swamp in the middle of the Syrian Desert. His visit to Damascus was only one of a series of daring canoe trips which he made in Europe, the Middle East, Russia and Armenia and which he later described in several books. He was the pioneer of British canoeing, and the name of his little craft became a household word in Victorian England.

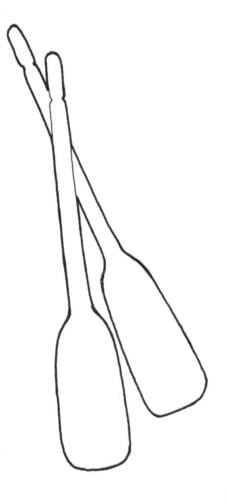

1. The best alternate title for this passage might be:
   - ☐ a. Through Damascus by Canoe.
   - ☐ b. John MacGregor—Canoist.
   - ☐ c. The "Rob Roy" Takes a Trip.
   - ☐ d. Scotch in Damascus.

2. The main idea of this passage centers around
   - ☐ a. adventure.
   - ☐ b. canoeing.
   - ☐ c. the Middle East.
   - ☐ d. the "Rob Roy."

3. How did John MacGregor get through to Damascus?
   - ☐ a. Through the mountains
   - ☐ b. Across a swamp
   - ☐ c. Across the Syrian Desert
   - ☐ d. Down the Barada River

4. John MacGregor seems to have had one outstanding characteristic:
   - ☐ a. lack of judgment.
   - ☐ b. courage.
   - ☐ c. sense of adventure.
   - ☐ d. recklessness.

5. The function of the first sentence is to arouse interest by presenting
   - ☐ a. a contrast.
   - ☐ b. a comparison.
   - ☐ c. an idea.
   - ☐ d. a definition.

6. The word pioneer means
   - ☐ a. designer.
   - ☐ b. enemy.
   - ☐ c. one who prepares the way for others.
   - ☐ d. one who gives money to benefit others.

CATEGORIES OF COMPREHENSION QUESTIONS

No. 1: Subject Matter	No. 3: Supporting Details	No. 5: Clarifying Devices
No. 2: Main Idea	No. 4: Conclusion	No. 6: Vocabulary in Context

83. COTTON

Cotton can grow almost any-where on dry loam topsoil at least eight inches deep, where there are six months of frost-free weather and twenty to thirty inches of rain. But with the increasing mechanization of cotton farming during the past twenty-five years, production has shifted sharply from the small, hilly farms of the Southeast to the big "ranches" of the Western plains where there are relative-ly few hillsides to bog down mechanical pickers or contour rows to harass four-row tractor rigs.

Today more than half of the nation's cotton is grown in Texas, California, Oklahoma, Arizona and New Mexico. The historic land of cotton has not been left in an economic vacuum however; the Southeast's former one-crop economy has been <u>diversified</u> by livestock, textile mills and other factories.

1. This passage is primarily about
  ☐ a. the production of cotton.
  ☐ b. techniques for growing cotton.
  ☐ c. the change in the areas for growing cotton.
  ☐ d. the areas where cotton may be grown.

2. The main thought of this passage is that
  ☐ a. cotton can be grown in certain areas under basic conditions.
  ☐ b. there has been an increasing mechanization of cotton farming.
  ☐ c. cotton is a fiber used to make cloth.
  ☐ d. cotton grows on dry loam soil.

3. Which of the following is true according to the passage?
  ☐ a. Cotton is grown in Texas, California, Oklahoma, Arkansas, and New Mexico.
  ☐ b. Half of the nation's cotton is grown in the Southeast states.
  ☐ c. Cotton can be grown on some small, hilly farms.
  ☐ d. Cotton farming has been going on for twenty-five years.

4. We can conclude from the passage that
  ☐ a. cotton was originally grown in the southeast United States.
  ☐ b. cotton is a most desirable fiber.
  ☐ c. cotton production in the U.S. was at one time concentrated in the Southeast.
  ☐ d. cotton can grow almost anywhere.

5. The author develops the passage by the use of
  ☐ a. comparison.
  ☐ b. contrast.
  ☐ c. description.
  ☐ d. arguments.

6. The word <u>diversified</u> is closest in meaning to
  ☐ a. consolidated.
  ☐ b. decreased.
  ☐ c. doubled.
  ☐ d. distributed.

CATEGORIES OF COMPREHENSION QUESTIONS

| No. 1: Subject Matter | No. 3: Supporting Details | No. 5: Clarifying Devices |
| No. 2: Main Idea | No. 4: Conclusion | No. 6: Vocabulary in Context |

---

84. NEVER ON SUNDAE

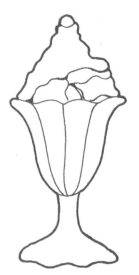

According to most historians the ice cream sundae has been on the American scene since the late 1890s, when it first appeared in Evanston, Illinois. Pious city fathers there, resenting the dissipating influence of the soda fountain, passed an ordinance forbidding the sale of ice cream sodas on Sunday. Some ingenious confectioners and drugstore operators, however, got around the law by serving ice cream with syrup—but without the soda.

The soda-less soda, called the Sunday soda, became so popular that orders for "Sundays" began to cross the counters on other days of the week as well. When the town fathers objected to a dish christened after the Lord's day, the spelling was changed to "sundae." Innovators have since added nuts, fruit, whipped cream and cherries. Today a deluxe sundae can cost several dollars and satisfy the hunger of two average eaters.

1. The best title for this selection would be:
   - ☐ a. Civil Disobedience in Evanston.
   - ☐ b. The Religious Significance of the Soda.
   - ☐ c. Confectioners Skirt the Law.
   - ☐ d. The Origin of the Ice Cream Sundae.

2. Restriction of the sale of ice cream sodas led to
   - ☐ a. the dissipation of the soda fountain's influence.
   - ☐ b. the invention of a new confection.
   - ☐ c. widespread civil disobedience.
   - ☐ d. greater religious observance of the Lord's day.

3. The ordinance prohibited the sale of
   - ☐ a. ice cream.
   - ☐ b. syrup.
   - ☐ c. ice cream sodas.
   - ☐ d. sundaes.

4. Changing the name of the dish to "sundae" was a
   - ☐ a. compromise.
   - ☐ b. profanity.
   - ☐ c. restriction.
   - ☐ d. prohibition.

5. The tone of the passage suggests that the author's attitude on the subject is one of
   - ☐ a. disrespect.
   - ☐ b. nonchalance.
   - ☐ c. amusement.
   - ☐ d. solemnity.

6. An institution which has a dissipating influence causes people to
   - ☐ a. waste money constantly.
   - ☐ b. seek unrestrained pleasure.
   - ☐ c. disperse aimlessly and recklessly.
   - ☐ d. ignore respect for tradition.

CATEGORIES OF COMPREHENSION QUESTIONS

No. 1: Subject Matter	No. 3: Supporting Details	No. 5: Clarifying Devices
No. 2: Main Idea	No. 4: Conclusion	No. 6: Vocabulary in Context

85. FIT TO SURVIVE

In the heart of the desert rain may not occur at all in a whole year. In summer, heat is scorching. July mean temperatures—the figure midway between the highest and lowest readings each day—sometimes exceed 95 degrees. Shade temperatures of 120 degrees are by no means unusual; and in winter bitterly cold days are not rare.

For mammals these conditions mean trouble. Vegetation is extremely sparse, creating a food problem and making concealment from predators difficult. (Conversely, of course, predatory animals have greater difficulty in approaching and capturing their prey undetected.) This lack of cover is a reason why nearly all desert mammals are nocturnal, leaving the security of their burrows or lairs only under the protection of darkness.

1. This passage is concerned with
   ☐ a. survival methods of desert animals.
   ☐ b. the effect of desert weather upon vegetation.
   ☐ c. weather conditions in the desert.
   ☐ d. the problems of mammals resulting from desert conditions.

2. The mammal on the desert is
   ☐ a. very likely to starve to death.
   ☐ b. an easy victim of predators.
   ☐ c. faced with problems caused by the environment.
   ☐ d. basically a predator.

3. The weather conditions in the heart of the desert are such that
   ☐ a. rain is frequent.
   ☐ b. the temperatures reach both high and low extremes.
   ☐ c. summers and winters are scorching.
   ☐ d. standing in the shade is the only means of escaping the unbearable heat.

4. The desert predators have difficulty in getting to their prey because of the
   ☐ a. difficulty of concealment.
   ☐ b. darkness of the nights.
   ☐ c. scorching heat.
   ☐ d. dense vegetation.

5. The author develops his point by the use of
   ☐ a. comparison and contrast.
   ☐ b. cause and effect.
   ☐ c. common sense.
   ☐ d. logical reasoning.

6. The word sparse is closest in meaning to
   ☐ a. brittle.
   ☐ b. harsh.
   ☐ c. thinly scattered.
   ☐ d. dried out.

CATEGORIES OF COMPREHENSION QUESTIONS

| No. 1: Subject Matter | No. 3: Supporting Details | No. 5: Clarifying Devices |
| No. 2: Main Idea | No. 4: Conclusion | No. 6: Vocabulary in Context |

86. MEN TAKE TO WATCHES

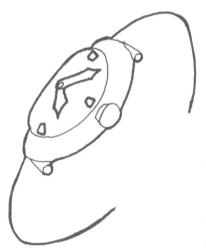

Wrist watches are an exception to the normal sequence in the evolution of men's jewelry. Reversing the usual order, they were first worn by women, then adopted by men. Queen Elizabeth and Napoleon's Josephine included wrist watches among their crown jewelry. After the turn of the century they were worn by Swiss mechanics and farm hands. Until World War I, Americans associated the wrist watch with flashy dressers and fortune hunters. Army officers and aviators then discovered that the wrist watch was the most practical timepiece for active combat. Indianapolis race car drivers later lent their prestige to the wrist watch. Several were given to Charles Lindbergh on the eve of his transatlantic flight. With such endorsements men dared to wear wrist watches without feeling self-conscious. By 1924 some 30 percent of men's watches were worn on the wrist. Today the figure is 90 percent.

1. This paragraph deals with the gradual process by which
   □ a. men invented the wrist watch.
   □ b. the wrist watch became popular for men.
   □ c. the usual order of evolution was reversed.
   □ d. prestigious individuals accepted the wrist watch.

2. Both men's and women's jewelry is affected by trends in
   □ a. popularity.
   □ b. practicality.
   □ c. prestige.
   □ d. value.

3. The wrist watch proved practical for military men first by
   □ a. the 1920s.
   □ b. the 1930s.
   □ c. World War I.
   □ d. World War II.

4. The paragraph suggests that under normal circumstances practical jewelry is worn
   □ a. first by men.
   □ b. first by women.
   □ c. by both men and women.
   □ d. when prestige is established.

5. The examples given by the author of the American men who first wore wrist watches serve
   □ a. to illustrate popularization.
   □ b. to reveal the associated prestige.
   □ c. to demonstrate the practicality.
   □ d. to reflect typological thinking.

6. The word <u>associated</u> means
   □ a. incorporated.
   □ b. understood.
   □ c. connected.
   □ d. seized.

CATEGORIES OF COMPREHENSION QUESTIONS

No. 1: Subject Matter	No. 3: Supporting Details	No. 5: Clarifying Devices
No. 2: Main Idea	No. 4: Conclusion	No. 6: Vocabulary in Context

87. ANCIENT MAN AT WAR

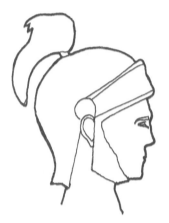 During one ancient battle the Egyptians were advancing on the city of Kadesh in central Syria. Somehow the four Egyptian regiments had spread out so far along the line of march that when the lead regiment was making camp before the walls of Kadesh, the second regiment was still crossing the Orontes River seven miles away. The other two regiments were even further behind. Suddenly, as the Egyptians began to ford the river, the enemy launched one of the great chariot attacks of ancient history. The charge demoralized the panic-stricken Egyptians and gave the attackers a swift, easy victory. For a few moments the power of mighty Egypt tottered dangerously. But then the enemy made a mistake. They paused to plunder the goods and weapons of the defeated army instead of pressing on. That gave the regiment at Kadesh time to march back to the river, where, in company with some newly arrived allies, they saved the day.

1. The best title for this selection would be:
   - ☐ a. Divide and Conquer.
   - ☐ b. The Fall of the Egyptian Empire.
   - ☐ c. The Battle of Kadesh.
   - ☐ d. Battle at the Orontes River.

2. The outcome of the battle was that
   - ☐ a. the Egyptians drove the enemy back to Kadesh.
   - ☐ b. the attackers captured the Egyptians.
   - ☐ c. Kadesh was captured.
   - ☐ d. neither side could claim a total victory.

3. The number of miles that the third Egyptian regiment lagged behind the first was
   - ☐ a. about seven.
   - ☐ b. more than seven.
   - ☐ c. less than seven.
   - ☐ d. less than two.

4. The most crucial mistake made by the attackers was that of
   - ☐ a. pausing to collect valuables.
   - ☐ b. using chariots.
   - ☐ c. attacking too early.
   - ☐ d. continuing the attack.

5. The author makes his point about the battle by
   - ☐ a. narration.
   - ☐ b. comparison.
   - ☐ c. persuasion.
   - ☐ d. contrast.

6. In this selection, demoralized means
   - ☐ a. defeated.
   - ☐ b. frightened.
   - ☐ c. confused.
   - ☐ d. inspired.

CATEGORIES OF COMPREHENSION QUESTIONS

No. 1: Subject Matter	No. 3: Supporting Details	No. 5: Clarifying Devices
No. 2: Main Idea	No. 4: Conclusion	No. 6: Vocabulary in Context

88. HANDMADE ICE CREAM

While electricity has displaced many hand-operated appliances, it has yet to overtake completely the old-fashioned ice cream freezers. The wooden tubs and the heavy metal cans were once all cranked by hand, requiring fifteen minutes of cranking to churn milk and powder and other foodstuffs into the nation's No. 1 dessert. The White Mountain Freezer Company of Nashua, New Hampshire, is the pioneer and leader in the industry. This company has produced more than 2,000,000 units in its 79-year history, and still makes most of its ice cream freezers in hand-crank models. Its larger sizes, designed primarily for institutional use, range up to 40-quart models, and are electrically operated.

The ice cream freezer is a product that was designed perfectly from the start. Except for minor improvements, the basic design has not changed since the first one was introduced. Nor, for that matter, has a better method been found for making ice cream at home.

1. The best title for this selection would be:
   □ a. Technological Advancement in Ice Cream Production.
   □ b. The Ice Cream Industry Today.
   □ c. The Old-Fashioned Ice Cream Freezer.
   □ d. The Nation's No. 1 Dessert.

2. The basic design of the hand-cranked ice cream freezer is ideally suited for
   □ a. institutional use.
   □ b. the dairy industry.
   □ c. home use.
   □ d. electric power.

3. Most of the ice cream freezers made by the White Mountain Freezer Company are
   □ a. hand-cranked.
   □ b. electrically operated.
   □ c. designed for institutions.
   □ d. large-sized.

4. The design of the ice cream freezer seems to be
   □ a. subject to change.
   □ b. ideal for mechanical operation.
   □ c. ideal for hand-cranked operation.
   □ d. almost perfect from the beginning.

5. The author mentions the White Mountain Freezer Company in order to
   □ a. show how old the machines are.
   □ b. illustrate a point.
   □ c. show how many different models there are.
   □ d. tell how many machines have been made.

6. The phrase designed primarily for institutional use suggests that the machine described is used
   □ a. where large quantities of ice cream are needed.
   □ b. in prisons and mental hospitals.
   □ c. in places where ice cream is enjoyed.
   □ d. wherever sufficient electricity is available.

CATEGORIES OF COMPREHENSION QUESTIONS

No. 1: Subject Matter	No. 3: Supporting Details	No. 5: Clarifying Devices
No. 2: Main Idea	No. 4: Conclusion	No. 6: Vocabulary in Context

89. MIRAGES

Since mirages are natural phenomena, they can be charted and photographed as well as seen. However, they do display one aspect which defies explanation. A law of physics states that the apparent size of an object diminishes at a rate inversely proportional to the square of its distance from an observer. An object whose distance from an observer is doubled, therefore, should appear one-quarter its former size. This rule conspicuously fails to apply to "long-distance" mirages which carry images of trees, ships, buildings and other objects a thousand or more miles, and set them up in the sky or on dry land, with no diminution in size. No one knows why.

In deserts, where conditions are close to ideal, some mirages appear almost as regularly as the morning sun. In some places mirages occur seasonally, and in others, infrequently or not at all. A village in Maryland has recorded only one mirage in its entire hundred-year history, but that one made up for what the town had been missing: a city of domed roofs appeared in the sky above it, perhaps coming all the way from North Africa or the Middle East.

1. This passage is mainly about mirages and
   ☐ a. the charting of them.
   ☐ b. their mystery and frequency.
   ☐ c. their exceptional appearance.
   ☐ d. the conditions making them possible.

2. An aspect of mirages that is unexplainable is the fact that they
   ☐ a. cannot be photographed.
   ☐ b. violate the laws of physics.
   ☐ c. can be transported so far.
   ☐ d. change sizes with the seasons.

3. Certain mirages appear regularly because of
   ☐ a. constant sun position.
   ☐ b. irregular ray reflection.
   ☐ c. constant atmospheric conditions.
   ☐ d. freak wind movements.

4. A mirage can show objects
   ☐ a. only over the desert.
   ☐ b. more than a thousand miles distant.
   ☐ c. only with a diminution in size.
   ☐ d. more easily over longer distances.

5. The author develops his point by means of
   ☐ a. logical reasoning.
   ☐ b. cause and effect narration.
   ☐ c. contrasting elements.
   ☐ d. citing examples.

6. A diminution is a
   ☐ a. reduction.
   ☐ b. change.
   ☐ c. enlargement.
   ☐ d. distortion.

CATEGORIES OF COMPREHENSION QUESTIONS

No. 1: Subject Matter	No. 3: Supporting Details	No. 5: Clarifying Devices
No. 2: Main Idea	No. 4: Conclusion	No. 6: Vocabulary in Context

90. CREATURES OF THE DRY WORLD

Many desert creatures are migrants and nomads, moving on when food and water become scarce. But desert snails aren't able to relocate, and they have acquired the ability to put themselves into "cold storage"—or, more correctly, into "nearly desiccated" storage. Two specimens of the desert snail were glued to cardboard and exhibited in the British Museum in 1846. Four years later an entomologist wondered what would happen if the dried-out creatures were placed in water. One actually revived!

Some desert animals emulate the snails, though not quite so dramatically. During hot summers and periods of drought they estivate—the word means "to pass the summer." Many reptiles estivate. Among the more accomplished are some water-storing frogs of the more arid regions of Australia and North America. The reservoir frog lives and breeds in pools which fill up in the rainy season. When the sun empties the pools, the frog goes down several feet into the mud, and after distending itself with water, shapes out a little moist cell whose walls later become dry, hard and insulating. There the frog, in a torpor that is profound though not as deep as that of hibernation, calmly sits it out until the next rainy season.

1. This selection deals mainly with
   - □ a. adaptation to cold.
   - □ b. adaptation to heat.
   - □ c. adaptation to dryness.
   - □ d. diversity of snails.

2. Estivating animals survive by
   - □ a. manufacturing water.
   - □ b. using less food.
   - □ c. migrating when food is scarce.
   - □ d. decreasing activity.

3. The frog prepares for the coming dry season by
   - □ a. burrowing into the mud.
   - □ b. storing food underground.
   - □ c. estivating during the wet season.
   - □ d. hibernating in an insulated cell.

4. The author implies that those animals that estivate are unable
   - □ a. to hibernate.
   - □ b. to desiccate.
   - □ c. to migrate.
   - □ d. to reproduce.

5. The author described the revival of the dried snail in order to illustrate
   - □ a. the process of estivation.
   - □ b. the method of cold hibernation.
   - □ c. the effectiveness of their technique.
   - □ d. the dependence on rainy seasons.

6. The word desiccated, as it is used in this selection, means
   - □ a. dried-up.
   - □ b. half-frozen.
   - □ c. distended.
   - □ d. insulated.

CATEGORIES OF COMPREHENSION QUESTIONS

No. 1: Subject Matter	No. 3: Supporting Details	No. 5: Clarifying Devices
No. 2: Main Idea	No. 4: Conclusion	No. 6: Vocabulary in Context

91. GREYHOUND OF THE DESERT

The saluqi may be the oldest purebred dog known to man. Egyptian tomb drawings from 4,000 B.C. show this lean, wind-swift hunter streaking after desert gazelles, and even earlier (6,000 B.C.) carvings show saluqis hunting gazelles. Pre-Islamic poems extolled "the fine-trained, lop-eared hounds with slender sides which lightly outran the sharp-horned white antelope." Two thousand years later the Egyptians mummified him, and Babylonian artists made carvings of him. The saluqi was referred to in Egyptian literature as The Noble One, Royal Dog of Egypt. His gaunt beauty was memorialized by Mogul miniaturists; Veronese frequently included him in canvases and frescoes; and Cellini saluted him in a bronze bas-relief. The speed and hunting prowess of the saluqi are often recited in Arabic odes. In the oral tradition of the vast Saudi Arabian desert his pedigree was passed on by word of mouth at the Bedouin gift-distributions of new litters. And today he courses after hare in the English countryside from Wiltshire to the Scottish border.

Little is known about the origin of the breed. Archaeology has provided pictorial evidence of its desert beginnings and long durability. But the name, as it now survives, suggests an ancient Arabic background.

1. The best title for this passage is:
   - ☐ a. Dogs of Ancient Egypt.
   - ☐ b. Saluqi: Extinct Purebred of Ancient Cultures.
   - ☐ c. Pedigrees of Arabia.
   - ☐ d. Saluqi: Noble Hound Dog of the Ages.

2. The saluqi was treasured primarily for his
   - ☐ a. majestic stance.
   - ☐ b. beautiful fur.
   - ☐ c. hunting prowess.
   - ☐ d. purebred strain.

3. Evidence of the purity of the saluqi strain was communicated
   - ☐ a. in ancient writings.
   - ☐ b. by the antiquity of the strain.
   - ☐ c. orally at gatherings.
   - ☐ d. at gift-distributions of new litters.

4. We might conclude from the appearance of the saluqi in ancient art works that this breed was
   - ☐ a. the most numerous.
   - ☐ b. the most sought after.
   - ☐ c. an invaluable asset.
   - ☐ d. a picturesque subject.

5. The author develops his main idea in this passage through the use of
   - ☐ a. historical references.
   - ☐ b. vivid description.
   - ☐ c. supportive examples.
   - ☐ d. flowing narration.

6. As used in the selection, prowess means
   - ☐ a. power.
   - ☐ b. skill.
   - ☐ c. beauty.
   - ☐ d. durability.

CATEGORIES OF COMPREHENSION QUESTIONS

No. 1: Subject Matter	No. 3: Supporting Details	No. 5: Clarifying Devices
No. 2: Main Idea	No. 4: Conclusion	No. 6: Vocabulary in Context

92. THE NATURE OF WATER

One of the earliest attempts to explain the nature of water was made by the Greek philosopher Aristotle in 335 B.C. when he issued his Theory of Matter. According to Aristotle's theory, every substance was a combination of four basic elements—fire, earth, air and water. This idea was to keep alchemists busy for centuries trying to change common metals into gold by rearranging their "elements." They were not very successful, however, since no one was ever able to break down a substance and find out just how much fire, earth, air and water was in it. Not until the eighteenth century did scientists decide that air, earth and fire were not really elements at all, and in 1781 a British chemist proved that water wasn't an element either.

That year Joseph Priestley exploded a mixture of air and hydrogen in a bottle as "a mere random experiment to entertain a few philosophical friends," and noted with interest that the explosion caused moisture to condense inside the bottle. He repeated the experiment until he was certain that the moisture was produced from the reaction of air and hydrogen, thereby proving that water, rather than being a basic element was itself composed of other chemicals.

In 1783 the French chemist Antoine Lavoisier elaborated on Priestley's experiment and discovered that the hydrogen was not combining with air to form water, but only with the oxygen in air. Further experiments determined that a molecule of water contained two atoms of hydrogen and one atom of oxygen, a chemical combination which has been given the symbol H_2O.

1. This passage is primarily about
   - □ a. the four basic elements.
   - □ b. eighteenth-century chemists.
   - □ c. the discovery of the composition of water.
   - □ d. the uses of water in chemistry.

2. According to French chemist Antoine Lavoisier what is not necessary to form water?
   - □ a. Oxygen
   - □ b. Air
   - □ c. Hydrogen
   - □ d. An explosion

3. The symbol H_2O represents the fact that a water molecule is made up of
   - □ a. one element.
   - □ b. two elements.
   - □ c. two molecules.
   - □ d. one atom.

4. Water is
   - □ a. a basic element.
   - □ b. a random mixture.
   - □ c. a combination of elements.
   - □ d. a chemical element.

5. The author discusses Aristotle's Theory of Matter in order
   - □ a. to disprove the theories of Lavoisier.
   - □ b. to exemplify the scientific method.
   - □ c. to illustrate early attempts to understand water.
   - □ d. to prove that water is one of the four basic elements.

6. In this example, the smallest unit which makes up water is
   - □ a. a molecule.
   - □ b. a chemical.
   - □ c. an atom.
   - □ d. an element.

CATEGORIES OF COMPREHENSION QUESTIONS

| No. 1: Subject Matter | No. 3: Supporting Details | No. 5: Clarifying Devices |
| No. 2: Main Idea | No. 4: Conclusion | No. 6: Vocabulary in Context |

93. MAPS BY CAMERA

The use of aerial photography as an aid in map making has been described by one writer as the greatest advance in cartography since the invention of the compass. The basic idea is well over 100 years old. In 1849, a French army engineer named Aime Laussedat made a series of photographs over Paris with ingenious combinations of balloons, kites and tiny sails. Early cameras secured to captive balloons were used to obtain topographic information in the United States during the Civil War. As techniques for making measurements in mapping became more refined, a new name was coined for the science: photogrammetry. Special applications of the principles of optics to steadily improving aerial cameras moved photogrammetry ahead, but the biggest breakthrough came, of course, with the appearance of the airplane.

The focal length of the aerial camera and the altitude from sea level, taking into account the average elevation above sea level of the terrain photographed, determine the scale of a vertical photograph taken from the air. In one mapping project involving the Arabian peninsula, because of the large area to be covered, it was decided to work with aerials made on the relatively small scale of 1: 60,000. This required the photography plane to fly at a constant 30,000 feet above the terrain level, or elevation, it was shooting—an elevation commonly traveled by today's jets. But the aircraft doing the photography was of a nonpressured variety, which meant that flight and photography crews had to be sustained by oxygen. At more than 5.6 miles up, even the air over the baking desert gets cold, with temperatures down to around minus 30 degrees. The men flying in that plane had to see to it that they were dressed for the occasion!

1. The passage is concerned with the
   - □ a. hardships involved in flying planes.
   - □ b. history of aerial photography.
   - □ c. role of aerial photography in map making.
   - □ d. value of cartography.

2. The main idea of the passage is that photogrammetry is
   - □ a. a great asset in map making.
   - □ b. relatively new.
   - □ c. a complicated science.
   - □ d. reliable.

3. Which of the following was not used to take the first aerial photographs?
   - □ a. Balloons
   - □ b. Gliders
   - □ c. Kites
   - □ d. Sails

4. The development of the airplane was a major breakthrough in photogrammetry because it
   - □ a. could fly even at night.
   - □ b. required less supervision.
   - □ c. could fly lower than former devices.
   - □ d. enabled the cameras to get a larger scope.

5. The author's tone in this passage is primarily
   - □ a. informative.
   - □ b. whimsical.
   - □ c. humorous.
   - □ d. helpful.

6. The business of making charts or maps is called
   - □ a. photogrammetry.
   - □ b. topology.
   - □ c. cartography.
   - □ d. aerial photography.

CATEGORIES OF COMPREHENSION QUESTIONS

No. 1: Subject Matter	No. 3: Supporting Details	No. 5: Clarifying Devices
No. 2: Main Idea	No. 4: Conclusion	No. 6: Vocabulary in Context

94. REFRESHMENT TIME

The coffee break as an organized American institution is relatively new. True, there have always been valiant souls who slip out for coffee at the corner drugstore. But as industry has become more and more solicitous of the welfare of the working man and woman, <u>surreptitious</u> disappearances from the office are almost extinct. Facts and figures substantiate an increased efficiency and morale among workers who have a coffee break in midmorning or midafternoon, and in some lucky instances, both times. The few minutes devoted to leisure and a touch of fellowship with colleagues refresh employees and send them back to work with renewed pep, statistics show.

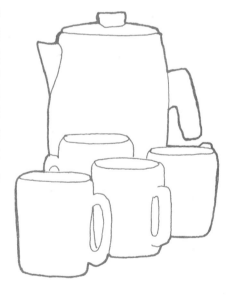

1. This selection is about
   - ☐ a. coffee as a stimulant.
   - ☐ b. employee morale.
   - ☐ c. the consumption of coffee.
   - ☐ d. the coffee break.

2. The coffee break is
   - ☐ a. an old American custom.
   - ☐ b. relatively new in America.
   - ☐ c. a means of avoiding boredom.
   - ☐ d. necessary to business success.

3. The coffee break leads to an increase in
   - ☐ a. worker efficiency.
   - ☐ b. employee attendance.
   - ☐ c. office fellowship.
   - ☐ d. satisfaction with one's job.

4. We can assume that the author
   - ☐ a. does not approve of the pause for coffee in the afternoon.
   - ☐ b. drinks a great deal of coffee.
   - ☐ c. thinks coffee renews energy.
   - ☐ d. believes that a short rest improves efficiency of workers.

5. The author's case relies on
   - ☐ a. hearsay.
   - ☐ b. statistics.
   - ☐ c. opinion.
   - ☐ d. estimates.

6. The word surreptitious means
   - ☐ a. illegal.
   - ☐ b. uncommon.
   - ☐ c. repeated.
   - ☐ d. secretive.

CATEGORIES OF COMPREHENSION QUESTIONS

No. 1: Subject Matter	No. 3: Supporting Details	No. 5: Clarifying Devices
No. 2: Main Idea	No. 4: Conclusion	No. 6: Vocabulary in Context

95. MOONSCAPE

After the invention of the telescope, the moon was mapped for the first time. Seventeenth- and eighteenth-century astronomers named the giant craters they discovered after the great scientists and philosophers of the past—Aristotle, Plato, Archimedes, and Copernicus. Galileo named the largest chain of mountains after the Apennines. He assumed that the large dark areas he saw, which were relatively free of mountains and craters, were stretches of water, and he named them seas: the Sea of Serenity, the Sea of Tranquility, the Ocean of the Rains, and the Ocean of Storms. These romantic appellations have remained, despite the fact that the absence of water on the moon has long been established.

1. The best title for this passage is:
   ☐ a. Giant Craters of the Moon.
   ☐ b. Men of the Moon.
   ☐ c. How Certain Areas of the Moon Were Named.
   ☐ d. Discoveries on the Moon.

2. The invention of the telescope made possible the
   ☐ a. location of the moon's seas.
   ☐ b. mapping of the moon.
   ☐ c. discovery of the moon.
   ☐ d. dispelling of romantic notions about the moon.

3. The Sea of Serenity
   ☐ a. once contained water.
   ☐ b. is not actually a sea.
   ☐ c. is the same as the Sea of Tranquility.
   ☐ d. is the largest crater on the moon.

4. One may infer from the passage, that during the seventeenth and eighteenth
   centuries
   ☐ a. misconceptions about the moon's geography existed.
   ☐ b. the telescope was invented.
   ☐ c. water was seen on the moon.
   ☐ d. Galileo was discovering giant craters on the moon.

5. The author develops his point by using
   ☐ a. cause and effect.
   ☐ b. historical and factual information.
   ☐ c. scientific observations.
   ☐ d. scientific data.

6. The word appellations means
   ☐ a. beliefs.
   ☐ b. fantasies.
   ☐ c. names.
   ☐ d. trends.

CATEGORIES OF COMPREHENSION QUESTIONS		
No. 1: Subject Matter	No. 3: Supporting Details	No. 5: Clarifying Devices
No. 2: Main Idea	No. 4: Conclusion	No. 6: Vocabulary in Context

96. THE CROCODILE'S TALE

The crocodile and the alligator are different species of Crocodilia. They have numerous minor differences in <u>anatomy</u> and habits, but are most easily distinguished by their shape, especially the shape of the snout. The most obvious difference between a crocodile and an alligator, for example, is that the alligator's snout is broad and rounded, while the crocodile has a more triangular head with a narrower, tapering snout.

Another difference is that the crocodile's fourth tooth on each side protrudes outward, but the alligator's fourth tooth fits into a socket in the upper jaw and is hidden from the outside. This extra-long tooth is for seizing the prey; the other teeth are for subsequent crunching and tearing.

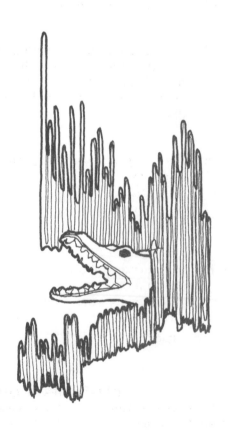

1. This article is mainly about
   □ a. the interesting aspects of crocodiles.
   □ b. the anatomy of reptiles.
   □ c. behavior patterns of the alligator and the crocodile.
   □ d. physical differences between two species of crocodilia.

2. The alligator and the crocodile
   □ a. can be distinguished by certain features.
   □ b. are openly hostile to each other.
   □ c. live in similar environments.
   □ d. are two of man's most dangerous enemies.

3. The snout difference between the alligator and the crocodile
   □ a. is an evolutionary adaptation.
   □ b. is a matter of size.
   □ c. is the most obvious distinguishing feature.
   □ d. can only be recognized by an expert.

4. We can assume that the alligator and the crocodile
   □ a. are often mistaken for each other.
   □ b. have similar teeth.
   □ c. use their different shaped snouts for different purposes.
   □ d. both possess a useless fourth tooth.

5. In developing his passage, the author uses
   □ a. analogies.
   □ b. comparison.
   □ c. scientific theories.
   □ d. narration.

6. The word <u>anatomy</u> most nearly means
   □ a. appearance.
   □ b. the structure of an animal.
   □ c. relative size.
   □ d. the stages of development.

CATEGORIES OF COMPREHENSION QUESTIONS

No. 1: Subject Matter	No. 3: Supporting Details	No. 5: Clarifying Devices
No. 2: Main Idea	No. 4: Conclusion	No. 6: Vocabulary in Context

97. THE COLEMAN LANTERN

The revival of antiquated articles may rest mightily on such simple reasons as the need for light. The Coleman Company of Wichita, Kansas, founded in 1903, was once the world's largest manufacturers of gasoline pressure lamps. Company officials thought for a while that progress was about to dim its lanterns. As federal rural electrification spread during the early 1930s, the farm market—80 percent of their production—declined. World War II <u>intervened</u> and the Coleman Company was called on to make a million of the lanterns for the armed forces. Today 90 percent of Coleman's 750,000 lanterns are sold annually for recreational purposes, largely as a result of the current emphasis on more outdoor family fun, on fishing, camping, hiking and picnicking.

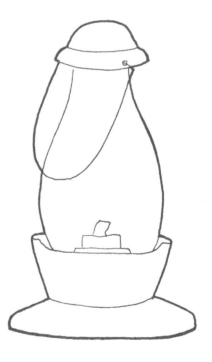

1. The best title for this selection would be:
   □ a. The Effect of the Recreation Boom.
   □ b. The Revival of Gasoline Lanterns.
   □ c. Outdoor Family Fun.
   □ d. The Intervention of World War II.

2. Today, most Coleman lanterns are used for
   □ a. rural home lighting.
   □ b. display as antiques.
   □ c. recreational purposes.
   □ d. military purposes.

3. According to the article, how many lanterns does Coleman sell in a year at present?
   □ a. One million
   □ b. Seven hundred and fifty thousand
   □ c. Ninety thousand
   □ d. Half a million

4. In the 1930s, what percent of Coleman's production was probably used for recreation?
   □ a. Eighty percent or greater
   □ b. Twenty-five percent
   □ c. Less than twenty percent
   □ d. Nearly fifty percent

5. When the author says of the Coleman Company that "progress was about to dim its lanterns," he means
   □ a. production was greater than ever.
   □ b. demand for lanterns increased.
   □ c. the company was about to fail.
   □ d. conditions were tranquil.

6. As it is used in this selection, the word or phrase closest in meaning to intervened is
   □ a. interfered.
   □ b. occurred.
   □ c. came in between.
   □ d. protected its interests.

CATEGORIES OF COMPREHENSION QUESTIONS

No. 1: Subject Matter	No. 3: Supporting Details	No. 5: Clarifying Devices
No. 2: Main Idea	No. 4: Conclusion	No. 6: Vocabulary in Context

98. ANCIENT MAN GOES TO WAR

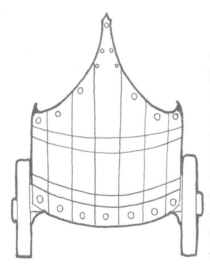

Military history actually begins with the Sumerians, people who inhabited southern Iraq and who left the first detailed records of their armies. As early as the first part of the third millennium B.C. the Sumerians had forged strong city-states and could field armies of great power and versatility. As was true of most ancient armies, the backbone of the Sumerians was the infantry. Their infantry was divided into light infantry companies, lightly clad mobile troops who fought with clubs, javelins and daggers, and heavy infantry companies, whose troops fought with a short, heavy spear. The Sumerians developed some surprises for their enemies, too. One was a method of attack: they marched into battle behind a solid row of shields, thus anticipating Alexander's Macedonian Phalanx by more than 2,000 years. The other surprise was a war chariot, the first known in history.

1. The best alternate title for this selection would be:
   - ☐ a. The Sumerian Army.
   - ☐ b. The First Soldiers.
   - ☐ c. The Origins of Modern Warfare.
   - ☐ d. The Earliest Known Armies.

2. Military history begins with the Sumerians because they were the first
   - ☐ a. to use the chariot.
   - ☐ b. to divide their infantry into companies.
   - ☐ c. to develop tactics and strategy.
   - ☐ d. to leave detailed records of their armies.

3. The principal difference between the light and heavy infantries was
   - ☐ a. the sizes of the soldiers.
   - ☐ b. their effectiveness in battle.
   - ☐ c. the types of weapons they used.
   - ☐ d. their degrees of mobility.

4. The Sumerian armies differed from their enemies by their use of
   - ☐ a. war chariots.
   - ☐ b. infantry troops.
   - ☐ c. javelins.
   - ☐ d. helmets.

5. The author mentions the later use of the phalanx to show that the Sumerians were more
   - ☐ a. dependent on their infantry.
   - ☐ b. advanced than their enemies.
   - ☐ c. innovative than their enemies.
   - ☐ d. disciplined than their enemies.

6. A <u>millenium</u> is a period of
   - ☐ a. a million years.
   - ☐ b. a thousand years.
   - ☐ c. a century.
   - ☐ d. a generation.

CATEGORIES OF COMPREHENSION QUESTIONS

No. 1: Subject Matter	No. 3: Supporting Details	No. 5: Clarifying Devices
No. 2: Main Idea	No. 4: Conclusion	No. 6: Vocabulary in Context

99. GEM OF GEMS

In 1612, as a 21-year-old prince, Shah Jehan married a beautiful and compassionate girl of 19. His inseparable companion, she continuously urged her devoted husband toward legal reforms and more peaceful ways. Because of her influence, when Shah Jehan became emperor, scholars and poets came to be more welcome at his court than soldiers. Today his brilliant 30-year reign is remembered as the golden age of Mogul literature, art and especially architecture.

There is a note of sadness, however, in the fact that the most beautiful example of all Mogul architecture—some argue even the most beautiful building in the world—was also due to the influence of the graceful lady on her loving husband. For the Taj Mahal, the mausoleum which bears her name, was inspired by his grief at her death at the age of 37. After eighteen years of marriage and a few brief years of Jehan's reign as emperor, Mumtaz Mahal died in 1631, bearing her fourteenth child.

1. This passage focuses on the
   - □ a. influence of the Shah's wife.
   - □ b. golden age of India.
   - □ c. building of the Taj Mahal.
   - □ d. reforms of Shah Jehan.

2. The author's main thought is that
   - □ a. the Shah built a monument to show how he grieved.
   - □ b. Mumtaz Mahal's life was cut short.
   - □ c. Mogul architecture is among the best in the world.
   - □ d. Mumtaz Mahal influenced the arts while she lived and after she died.

3. The author tells us the Shah's reforms reflected his wife's
   - □ a. example.
   - □ b. wishes.
   - □ c. devotion.
   - □ d. beauty.

4. In this passage, the author would agree that the Taj Mahal is
   - □ a. unsurpassed in beauty.
   - □ b. a splendid tribute.
   - □ c. an inspiration.
   - □ d. evidence of artistic advance.

5. According to the author, the selection bears "a note of sadness." We are made to feel this through the author's mentioning of
   - □ a. the Shah's grief at his wife's death and the beauty of her memorial.
   - □ b. the vivid description of the Taj Mahal.
   - □ c. the story of the building of the mausoleum.
   - □ d. the foolishness of building a beautiful building as a symbol of love for someone who has died.

6. A mausoleum is best defined as a kind of
   - □ a. building and gardens.
   - □ b. museum and art gallery.
   - □ c. monument and tomb.
   - □ d. mosque for worship.

CATEGORIES OF COMPREHENSION QUESTIONS

No. 1: Subject Matter	No. 3: Supporting Details	No. 5: Clarifying Devices
No. 2: Main Idea	No. 4: Conclusion	No. 6: Vocabulary in Context

100. DISTANT RELATIONS

Years ago, Norwegian archaeologist Thor Heyerdahl began to wonder why it was that when 15th- and 16th-century Spanish explorers "discovered" Central and South America, they found astonishingly advanced civilizations—Aztec, Mayan, Incan—along with traditions suggesting that white men resembling the Spaniards had come centuries before.

Particularly intriguing was the indisputable similarity of reed boats painted on tombs in Egypt to reed boats painted on ceramic pots in Peru. Further, boats still used today on Easter Island on the Pacific side of South America resemble those sailed on Lake Titicaca in the high Andes.

Was it likely that boats so nearly identical had developed independently of each other? Some archaeologists said yes, but Heyerdahl thought it was much more probable that the boats, as well as nearly 50 other features similar to both ancient Egypt and ancient Peru, had been imported.

This would imply, however, that Egyptians—or *someone* from the Mediterranean—sailed across the formidable South Atlantic in apparently fragile, unseaworthy boats made of papyrus from reeds that once grew in profusion along the Nile. Was this possible? Heyerdahl, who had already floated across the Pacific on the now-famous balsa raft, *Kon-Tiki,* to prove an earlier theory, decided there was only one way to find out: build a papyrus boat and sail it to South America. After two tries, he did it, proving that someone *could have* done it, if not that they *did* do it, or who "they" were.

1. This passage is concerned with the
   - ☐ a. way to build and sail a papyrus boat.
   - ☐ b. possibility of Peruvian and Egyptian civilizations being related.
   - ☐ c. discovery of South America.
   - ☐ d. designs on Egyptian tombs.

2. Thor Heyerdahl feels that
   - ☐ a. the Aztecs of Peru are the descendants of an Indian tribe in Egypt.
   - ☐ b. anyone could have sailed a boat from Egypt to South America.
   - ☐ c. Spaniards were the first to discover South America.
   - ☐ d. South American culture may be connected to Egyptian culture.

3. The boat which Thor Heyerdahl built and sailed from Egypt to South America was made of
   - ☐ a. papyrus.
   - ☐ b. old ceramic pots.
   - ☐ c. weeds.
   - ☐ d. driftwood.

4. Thor Heyerdahl believes, as a result of his boat trip, that Peru and Egypt are
   - ☐ a. definitely connected.
   - ☐ b. only coincidentally connected.
   - ☐ c. possibly connected.
   - ☐ d. definitely not connected.

5. The italics in the passage (*could have* and *did*) serve
   - ☐ a. no necessary function.
   - ☐ b. to show that Mr. Heyerdahl's opinion differs from those of other archaeologists.
   - ☐ c. to remind the reader that the present is simply an extension of the past.
   - ☐ d. to emphasize the possibility of sailing a small boat from Egypt to South America.

6. The word papyrus as used in the passage means
   - ☐ a. fine paper.
   - ☐ b. a type of plant.
   - ☐ c. a scroll.
   - ☐ d. a type of boat.

CATEGORIES OF COMPREHENSION QUESTIONS

No. 1: Subject Matter	No. 3: Supporting Details	No. 5: Clarifying Devices
No. 2: Main Idea	No. 4: Conclusion	No. 6: Vocabulary in Context

Answer Key

Passage 1:	1-c	2-c	3-a	4-d	5-d	6-b
Passage 2:	1-a	2-a	3-a	4-a	5-b	6-d
Passage 3:	1-b	2-d	3-a	4-c	5-a	6-c
Passage 4:	1-c	2-d	3-c	4-a	5-b	6-a
Passage 5:	1-c	2-a	3-d	4-b	5-d	6-d
Passage 6:	1-b	2-c	3-b	4-b	5-c	6-c
Passage 7:	1-c	2-a	3-d	4-a	5-c	6-b
Passage 8:	1-c	2-c	3-d	4-b	5-a	6-a
Passage 9:	1-c	2-d	3-c	4-a	5-b	6-c
Passage 10:	1-c	2-a	3-c	4-c	5-b	6-c
Passage 11:	1-c	2-b	3-d	4-d	5-a	6-c
Passage 12:	1-a	2-a	3-c	4-b	5-c	6-c
Passage 13:	1-a	2-b	3-d	4-b	5-a	6-b
Passage 14:	1-a	2-c	3-d	4-d	5-d	6-b
Passage 15:	1-b	2-b	3-b	4-a	5-b	6-b
Passage 16:	1-b	2-b	3-c	4-d	5-b	6-a
Passage 17:	1-c	2-d	3-c	4-b	5-b	6-b
Passage 18:	1-a	2-a	3-d	4-a	5-c	6-b
Passage 19:	1-a	2-b	3-a	4-d	5-d	6-b
Passage 20:	1-c	2-d	3-d	4-a	5-d	6-c
Passage 21:	1-c	2-b	3-d	4-a	5-c	6-d
Passage 22:	1-b	2-d	3-b	4-a	5-a	6-b
Passage 23:	1-b	2-c	3-a	4-b	5-a	6-c
Passage 24:	1-c	2-d	3-c	4-c	5-b	6-b
Passage 25:	1-d	2-c	3-b	4-b	5-a	6-b

Passage 26:	1-a	2-c	3-c	4-d	5-b	6-a
Passage 27:	1-c	2-d	3-d	4-a	5-b	6-c
Passage 28:	1-b	2-d	3-a	4-a	5-a	6-d
Passage 29:	1-b	2-a	3-d	4-c	5-a	6-b
Passage 30:	1-a	2-a	3-c	4-b	5-d	6-b
Passage 31:	1-b	2-c	3-c	4-d	5-a	6-c
Passage 32:	1-b	2-a	3-c	4-a	5-b	6-d
Passage 33:	1-c	2-b	3-d	4-a	5-b	6-c
Passage 34:	1-d	2-b	3-c	4-a	5-d	6-b
Passage 35:	1-c	2-d	3-a	4-b	5-d	6-c
Passage 36:	1-b	2-a	3-d	4-c	5-d	6-a
Passage 37:	1-c	2-d	3-b	4-d	5-a	6-b
Passage 38:	1-c	2-d	3-d	4-b	5-a	6-c
Passage 39:	1-a	2-b	3-c	4-a	5-b	6-d
Passage 40:	1-b	2-a	3-d	4-b	5-c	6-a
Passage 41:	1-d	2-d	3-c	4-b	5-b	6-c
Passage 42:	1-b	2-c	3-a	4-d	5-c	6-d
Passage 43:	1-b	2-d	3-c	4-b	5-a	6-c
Passage 44:	1-b	2-c	3-b	4-d	5-a	6-b
Passage 45:	1-b	2-b	3-b	4-a	5-b	6-b
Passage 46:	1-c	2-a	3-c	4-b	5-d	6-d
Passage 47:	1-b	2-a	3-d	4-a	5-a	6-c
Passage 48:	1-b	2-a	3-c	4-a	5-a	6-c
Passage 49:	1-c	2-d	3-c	4-a	5-b	6-b
Passage 50:	1-a	2-a	3-c	4-a	5-a	6-c

Passage 51:	1-a	2-c	3-c	4-b	5-d	6-b
Passage 52:	1-c	2-c	3-b	4-b	5-c	6-b
Passage 53:	1-c	2-a	3-b	4-d	5-d	6-c
Passage 54:	1-c	2-b	3-d	4-d	5-c	6-c
Passage 55:	1-c	2-b	3-c	4-b	5-a	6-b
Passage 56:	1-c	2-b	3-a	4-d	5-c	6-d
Passage 57:	1-d	2-a	3-b	4-b	5-d	6-a
Passage 58:	1-c	2-d	3-a	4-d	5-b	6-c
Passage 59:	1-a	2-d	3-b	4-b	5-d	6-a
Passage 60:	1-b	2-b	3-d	4-b	5-c	6-c
Passage 61:	1-b	2-a	3-c	4-d	5-b	6-c
Passage 62:	1-c	2-b	3-d	4-a	5-c	6-a
Passage 63:	1-c	2-b	3-d	4-d	5-b	6-a
Passage 64:	1-c	2-c	3-a	4-b	5-c	6-a
Passage 65:	1-b	2-c	3-b	4-b	5-b	6-a
Passage 66:	1-a	2-c	3-d	4-b	5-d	6-a
Passage 67:	1-b	2-d	3-a	4-c	5-d	6-b
Passage 68:	1-c	2-a	3-d	4-d	5-a	6-b
Passage 69:	1-a	2-a	3-d	4-c	5-a	6-c
Passage 70:	1-c	2-b	3-d	4-b	5-b	6-a
Passage 71:	1-d	2-c	3-a	4-b	5-c	6-b
Passage 72:	1-b	2-c	3-d	4-b	5-c	6-a
Passage 73:	1-d	2-a	3-b	4-b	5-d	6-a
Passage 74:	1-b	2-a	3-c	4-a	5-b	6-d
Passage 75:	1-b	2-c	3-a	4-b	5-c	6-a

Passage 76:	1-b	2-b	3-c	4-b	5-b	6-b
Passage 77:	1-b	2-a	3-d	4-b	5-d	6-d
Passage 78:	1-c	2-c	3-d	4-b	5-b	6-b
Passage 79:	1-b	2-b	3-b	4-c	5-a	6-b
Passage 80:	1-a	2-a	3-d	4-b	5-c	6-a
Passage 81:	1-a	2-a	3-d	4-d	5-c	6-c
Passage 82:	1-b	2-b	3-d	4-c	5-a	6-c
Passage 83:	1-c	2-b	3-c	4-c	5-c	6-d
Passage 84:	1-d	2-b	3-c	4-a	5-c	6-b
Passage 85:	1-d	2-c	3-b	4-a	5-b	6-c
Passage 86:	1-b	2-a	3-c	4-a	5-c	6-c
Passage 87:	1-d	2-d	3-b	4-a	5-a	6-c
Passage 88:	1-c	2-c	3-a	4-d	5-b	6-a
Passage 89:	1-b	2-b	3-c	4-b	5-d	6-a
Passage 90:	1-c	2-d	3-a	4-c	5-c	6-a
Passage 91:	1-d	2-c	3-d	4-d	5-a	6-b
Passage 92:	1-c	2-b	3-b	4-c	5-c	6-c
Passage 93:	1-c	2-a	3-b	4-d	5-a	6-c
Passage 94:	1-d	2-b	3-a	4-d	5-b	6-d
Passage 95:	1-c	2-b	3-b	4-a	5-b	6-c
Passage 96:	1-d	2-a	3-c	4-a	5-b	6-b
Passage 97:	1-b	2-c	3-b	4-c	5-c	6-c
Passage 98:	1-a	2-d	3-c	4-a	5-b	6-b
Passage 99:	1-a	2-d	3-b	4-b	5-a	6-c
Passage 100:	1-b	2-d	3-a	4-c	5-d	6-b

Diagnostic Charts
Progress Graphs

DIAGNOSTIC CHART

READING PASSAGE::

CATEGORIES OF COMPREHENSION SKILLS	1	2	3	4	5	6	7	8	9	10	11	12	13	14	15	16	17	18	19	20	21	22	23	24	25
1. SUBJECT MATTER																									
2. MAIN IDEAS																									
3. SUPPORTING DETAILS																									
4. CONCLUSIONS																									
5. CLARIFYING DEVICES																									
6. VOCABULARY																									

GRAPHING YOUR PROGRESS

	1	2	3	4	5	6	7	8	9	10	11	12	13	14	15	16	17	18	19	20	21	22	23	24	25
6 CORRECT = 100%																									
5 CORRECT = 83%																									
4 CORRECT = 67%																									
3 CORRECT = 50%																									
2 CORRECT = 33%																									
1 CORRECT = 17%																									

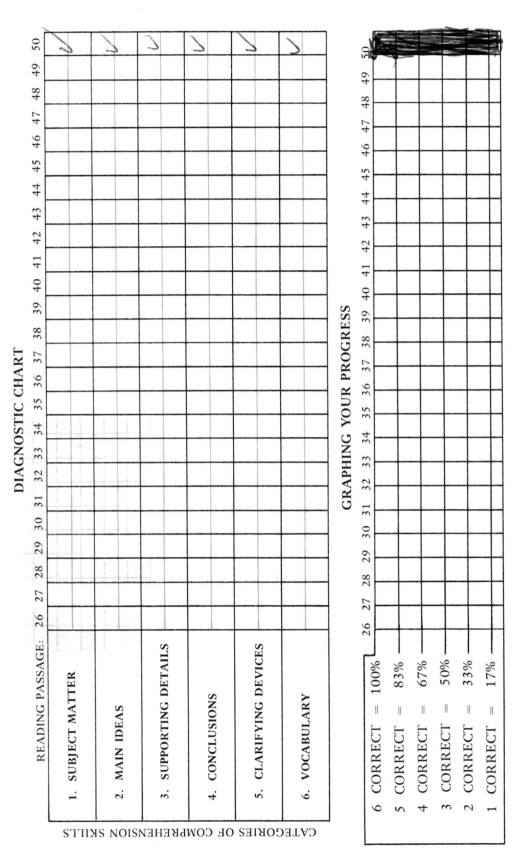

DIAGNOSTIC CHART

READING PASSAGE: 26 27 28 29 30 31 32 33 34 35 36 37 38 39 40 41 42 43 44 45 46 47 48 49 50

CATEGORIES OF COMPREHENSION SKILLS

1. SUBJECT MATTER

2. MAIN IDEAS

3. SUPPORTING DETAILS

4. CONCLUSIONS

5. CLARIFYING DEVICES

6. VOCABULARY

GRAPHING YOUR PROGRESS

26 27 28 29 30 31 32 33 34 35 36 37 38 39 40 41 42 43 44 45 46 47 48 49 50

6 CORRECT = 100%

5 CORRECT = 83%

4 CORRECT = 67%

3 CORRECT = 50%

2 CORRECT = 33%

1 CORRECT = 17%

221

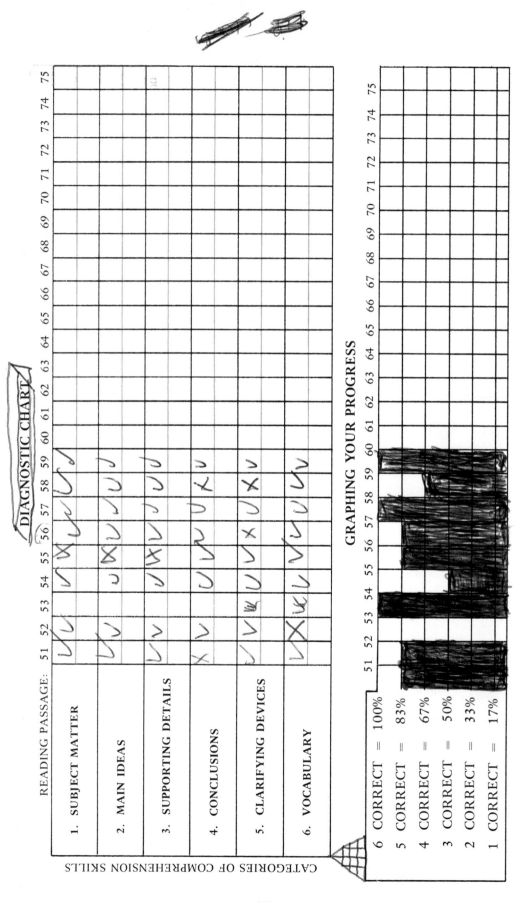

DIAGNOSTIC CHART

READING PASSAGE: | 51 | 52 | 53 | 54 | 55 | 56 | 57 | 58 | 59 | 60 | 61 | 62 | 63 | 64 | 65 | 66 | 67 | 68 | 69 | 70 | 71 | 72 | 73 | 74 | 75

CATEGORIES OF COMPREHENSION SKILLS

1. SUBJECT MATTER
2. MAIN IDEAS
3. SUPPORTING DETAILS
4. CONCLUSIONS
5. CLARIFYING DEVICES
6. VOCABULARY

GRAPHING YOUR PROGRESS

| 51 | 52 | 53 | 54 | 55 | 56 | 57 | 58 | 59 | 60 | 61 | 62 | 63 | 64 | 65 | 66 | 67 | 68 | 69 | 70 | 71 | 72 | 73 | 74 | 75

6 CORRECT = 100%
5 CORRECT = 83%
4 CORRECT = 67%
3 CORRECT = 50%
2 CORRECT = 33%
1 CORRECT = 17%